Student Workbook with Practice Tests and PowerPoint® Lecture Outlines

for

Henslin

Essentials of Sociology
A Down-to-Earth Approach

Sixth Edition

prepared by

Beth Tracton-Bishop
College of St. Elizabeth

PEARSON

Boston   New York   San Francisco
Mexico City   Montreal   Toronto   London   Madrid   Munich   Paris
Hong Kong   Singapore   Tokyo   Cape Town   Sydney

ISBN 0-205-46717-2

Printed in the United States of America

10 9 8 7 6 5 4 3   10 09 08 07 06

Table of Contents

CHAPTER 1

THE SOCIOLOGICAL PERSPECTIVE

KEY TERMS

applied sociology: sociology that is used to solve social problems—from the micro level of family relationships to the macro level of war and pollution

basic (or pure) sociology: sociological research whose only purpose is to make discoveries about life in human groups, not to make changes in those groups

bourgeoisie: those people who own the means to produce wealth

class conflict: Karl Marx's term for the struggle between owners (the bourgeoisie) and workers (the proletariat)

closed-ended questions: questions followed by a list of possible answers to be selected by the respondent

conflict theory: a theoretical framework in which society is viewed as composed of groups competing for scarce resources

control group: a group of subjects not exposed to the independent variable

dependent variable: a factor that is changed by an independent variable

documents: in its narrow sense, written sources that provide data; in its extended sense, archival material of any sort, including photographs, movies, and so on

experiment: the use of control groups and experimental groups and dependent and independent variables to test causation

experimental group: the group of subjects exposed to the independent variable

functional analysis: a theoretical framework in which society is viewed as a whole unit, composed of interrelated parts, each with a function that, when fulfilled, contributes to society's equilibrium; also known as functionalism and structural functionalism

hypothesis: a statement of the expected relationship between variables according to predictions from a theory

independent variable: a factor that causes a change in another variable, called the *dependent variable*

latent function: unintended consequences that help social systems adjust

latent dysfunction: unintended consequences that undermine a system's equilibrium

macro-level analysis: an examination of large-scale patterns of society

manifest function: an action that is intended to help some part of the system

micro-level analysis: an examination of small-scale patterns of society

nonverbal interaction: communication without words through gestures, space, silence, and so on

open-ended questions: questions that respondents are able to answer in their own words

operational definition: the way in which a variable in a hypothesis is measured

participant observation (or fieldwork): research in which a researcher *participates* in a research setting while *observing* what is happening in that setting

population: the target group to be studied

positivism: the application of the scientific approach to the social world

proletariat: the mass of workers

random sample: a sample in which everyone in the target population has the same chance of being included in the study

rapport: a feeling of trust between researchers and subjects

reliability: the extent to which data produce consistent results

replication: repeating a study in order to test its findings

research method (or research design): one of six procedures sociologists use to collect data: surveys, participant observation, secondary analysis, documents, unobtrusive measure, and experiments

respondents: people who respond to a survey, either in interviews or by self-administered questionnaires

secondary analysis: the analysis of data already collected by other researchers

social facts: patterns of behavior that reflect some underlying condition of society

social Darwinism: the idea that societies evolve from lower to higher forms

social integration: the degree to which people are tied to their social groups

social interaction: what people do when they are in one another's presence

social location: the groups people belong to because of their location in history and society

society: a group of people who share a culture and a territory

sociological perspective: an approach that seeks to understand human behavior by placing it within its broader social context

sociology: the scientific study of society and human behavior

stratified random sample: a sample of specific subgroups of the target population in which everyone in the subgroups has an equal chance of being included in the study

survey: collecting data by having people answer a series of questions

symbolic interaction: a theoretical perspective that focuses on how people use symbols to establish meaning, develop their views of the world, and communicate with one another

theory: a general statement about how some parts of the world fit together and how they work; and explanation of how two or more facts are related to one another

unobtrusive measures: observing people in such a way that they do not know they are being studied

validity: the extent to which an operational definition measures what was intended

value free: the view that a sociologist's personal values or biases should not influence social research

values: ideas about what is good or worthwhile in life; attitudes about the way the world ought to be; the standards by which people define what is desirable or undesirable, good or bad, beautiful or ugly

variable: a factor thought to be significant for human behavior, which varies from one case to another

KEY PEOPLE

Jane Addams: Addams was the founder of Hull House—a settlement house in the immigrant community of Chicago. She invited sociologists from nearby University of Chicago to visit. In 1931 she was a winner of the Nobel Peace Prize.

Mario Brajuha: During an investigation into a restaurant fire, officials subpoenaed notes taken by this sociologist in connection with his **participant observation research** on restaurant work. He was threatened with jail but would not turn over his notes.

Auguste Comte: Comte is often credited with being the founder of sociology, because he was the first to suggest that the scientific method be applied to the study of the social world.

Lewis Coser: Coser pointed out that conflict is likely to develop among people in close relationships because they are connected by a network of responsibilities, power and rewards.

Ralf Dahrendorf: Dahrendorf's work is associated with the **conflict perspective**. He suggested that conflict is inherent in all relations that have authority.

W.E.B. DuBois: DuBois was the first African American to earn a doctorate at Harvard University. For most of his career, he taught sociology at Atlanta University. He was concerned about social injustice, wrote about race relations, and was one of the founders of the National Association for the Advancement of Colored People.

Emile Durkheim: Durkheim was responsible for getting sociology recognized as a separate discipline. He was interested in studying how social forces shape individual behavior. He stressed that sociologist should use **social facts**—patterns of behavior that reflect some underlying condition of society

Laud Humphreys: The sociologist carried out doctoral research on homosexual activity. In order to obtain information, he misrepresented himself to his research subjects. When his methods became widely known, a debate developed over his use of questionable ethics.

Harriet Martineau: An Englishwoman who studied British and United States social life and published *Society in America* decades before either Durkheim or Weber was born.

Karl Marx: Marx believed that social development grew out of conflict between social classes; under capitalism, this conflict was between the *bourgeoisie*—those who own the means to produce wealth—and the *proletariat*—the mass of workers. His work is associated with the conflict perspective.

Robert Merton: Merton contributed the terms *manifest and latent functions* and *latent dysfunctions* to the functionalist perspective.

Wright Mills: Mills suggested that external influences—or a person's experiences—become part of his or her thinking and motivations and explain social behavior. In the 1950s he urged United States sociologists to get back to social reform. He argued that research without theory is of little value, simply a collection of unrelated *facts*, and theory that is unconnected to research is abstract and empty, unlikely to represent the way life really is.

Talcott Parsons: Parsons' work dominated sociology in the 1940s–1950s. He developed abstract models of how the parts of society harmoniously work together.

Herbert Spencer: Another early social philosopher, Spencer believed that societies evolve from barbarian to civilized forms. The first to use the expression "the survival of the fittest" to reflect his belief that social evolution depended on the survival of the most capable and intelligent and the extinction of the less capable. His views became known as *social Darwinism*.

Max Weber: Among Weber's many contributions to sociology were his study of the relationship between the emergence of Protestant belief system and the rise of capitalism. He believed that sociologists should not allow their personal values to affect their social research and objectivity should become the hallmark of sociology.

Essentials of Sociology

Sixth Edition

Chapter One:
The Sociological
Perspective

Chapter Overview

- ❖ The Sociological Perspective
- ❖ The Origins of Sociology
- ❖ Sexism in Early Sociology
- ❖ Sociology in North America
- ❖ Theoretical Perspectives in Sociology
- ❖ Doing Sociological Research
- ❖ Research Methods
- ❖ Ethics in Sociological Research

Copyright © Allyn & Bacon 2006   2

Seeing the Broader Social Context

❖ How Groups Influence People

❖ How People are Influenced by Their

Society

  ❖ People Who Share a Culture

  ❖ People Who Share a Territory

Copyright © Allyn & Bacon 2006   3

Social Location
Corners in Life

❖Jobs ❖Gender

❖Income ❖Age

❖Education ❖Race

4

Origins of Sociology
Tradition vs. Science

❖Superstition & Myth

❖Science - Develop Theories and Test

❖Sociology Grew From Social Upheaval in Industrial Revolution

❖French and American Revolutions Encouraged New Thought

❖Introduction of Scientific Method
5

Auguste Compte
Positivism

❖Applying the Scientific Method to Social World

❖Coined the Phrase "Sociology"

❖"Armchair Philosophy"

❖Observe Society to Uncover Fundamental Laws

1798-1857

6

Herbert Spencer
Social Darwinism

❖Second Founder of Sociology

❖Reform Not Goal of Sociology

❖Lower and Higher Forms of Society

❖Coined Phrase "Survival of the Fittest"

7

Karl Marx
Class Conflict

❖Engine of Human History is Class Conflict

❖The Bourgeoisie vs. The Proletariat

❖Marxism not the Same as Communism

1818-1883

8

Emile Durkheim
Social Integration

❖Got Sociology Recognized as Separate Discipline

❖Studied How Social Forces Affect Behavior

❖Identified "Social Integration" - Degree to Which People are Tied to Social Group

1858-1917

Max Weber

The Protestant Ethic

1864-1920

❖Religion and the Origin

of Capitalism

❖Religion is Central

Force in Social Change

❖Protestant Ethic and

Spirit of Capitalism

10

Sexism in Early Sociology

❖Attitudes of the Time
  ❖1800's Sex Roles Rigidly
    Defined
  ❖Few People Educated
    Beyond Basics
❖Harriet Martineau
  ❖Published *Society in America*
    Before Durkheim and Weber
    Were Born
  ❖Her Work was Ignored

Harriet Martineau

1802-1876

11

Sociology in North America

❖Early History: Tension Between Social

Reform and Sociological Analysis

❖Jane Addams and Social Reform

❖W. E. B. Du Bois and Race Relations

Jane Addams

1860-1935

12

Sociology in North America (con't)

❖Talcott Parsons and C. Wright Mills: Theory vs. Reform

❖Continuing Tension and Rise of Applied Sociology

13

Theoretical Perspectives

❖Symbolic Interactionism - Symbols in Everyday Life

❖Applying Symbolic Interactionism - Changing the Meaning of Symbols Affects Expectations

14

Applying Symbolic Interactionism - Examples

❖Meaning of Marriage and Divorce

Φ The Meaning of Parenthood

❖The Meaning of Children

15

Functional Analysis

❖ Society is a Whole Unit Made Up of

Interrelated Parts that Work Together

❖ Robert Merton - Intention and Manifest

Function

❖ Function and Dysfunction

Copyright © Allyn & Bacon 2006   16

Applying Functional Analysis

❖ Industrialization Undermines Traditional

Family Functions

   ❖ Household Tasks

   ❖ Education of Children

   ❖ Care of the Sick and Elderly

Copyright © Allyn & Bacon 2006   17

Conflict Theory

❖ Karl Marx and Conflict Theory

❖ Conflict Theory Today

❖ Feminists and Conflict Theory

❖ Applying Conflict Theory

Copyright © Allyn & Bacon 2006   18

Levels of Analysis

❖Macro Level - Large Scale

Patterns in Society

❖Micro Level - Social

Interactions in Small Scale

Patterns

Copyright © Allyn & Bacon 2006

Levels of Analysis: Macro and Micro

❖Functionalists and Conflict Theorists

Focus on the Macro Level

❖Symbolic Interactionists Focus on the

Micro Level

Copyright © Allyn & Bacon 2006   20

Putting the Theoretical Perspectives Together

❖Perspectives Provide Contrasting Views

❖Each Provides a Distinctive Interpretation

❖Combining Perspectives is a More

Comprehensive Approach

Copyright © Allyn & Bacon 2006   21

Doing Sociological Research

❖The Scientific Research Model Follows Eight Basic Steps:

(1) Selecting a topic

(5) Choosing a research method

(2) Defining the problem

(6) Collecting the data

(3) Reviewing the literature

(7) Analyzing the results

(4) Formulating a hypothesis

(8) Sharing the results

Copyright © Allyn & Bacon 2006   22

Doing Research - Surveys

❖Select a Sample
  - ❖ Random
  - ❖ Stratified Random

❖Ask Questions
  - ❖ Neutral
  - ❖ Open-Ended
  - ❖ Closed-Ended

❖Establish Rapport

Copyright © Allyn & Bacon 2006   23

Doing Research - Participant Observation

❖Researcher Participates in Research Setting While Observing

❖Unobtrusive Measures—When Researchers Observe People Unbeknownst to Them

❖Secondary Analysis

Copyright © Allyn & Bacon 2006   24

Doing Experiments

❖In doing experiments, you randomly divide subjects into two groups:

  ❖The experimental group—those exposed to the independent variable (something that causes a change)

  ❖The control group—those not exposed to the independent variable.

Copyright © Allyn & Bacon 2006   25

Ethics in Sociological Research

❖Ethics Require Openness, Honesty, and Truth

❖Ethics Condemn Plagiarism.

❖Research Participants should not be Harmed.

Copyright © Allyn & Bacon 2006   26

Ethics in Sociological Research

❖Protecting Subjects - Brajuha Research

❖Misleading Subjects - Humphreys Research

❖Values in Sociological Research

Copyright © Allyn & Bacon 2006   27

Essentials of Sociology

Sixth Edition

Chapter One:
The Sociological
Perspective

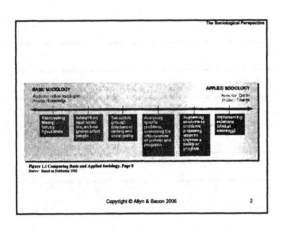

Figure 1.1 Comparing Basic and Applied Sociology. Page 8
Source: Based on DeMartini 1982.

2

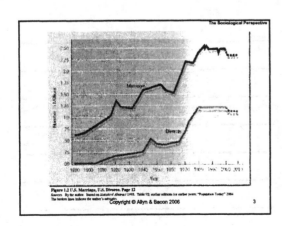

Figure 1.2 U.S. Marriage, U.S. Divorce. Page 12
Sources: By the author. Based on Statistical Abstract 1995: Table 92; earlier editions for earlier years; "Population Today" 2004
The broken lines indicate the author's estimates.

3

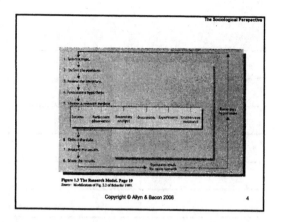

Figure 1.3 The Research Model. Page 19
Source: Modification of Fig. 2.2 of Schaefer 1989.

4

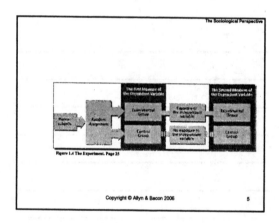

Figure 1.4 The Experiment. Page 25

5

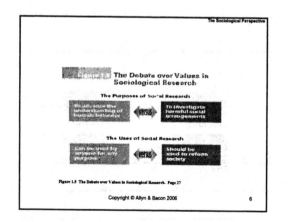

Figure 1.5 The Debate over Values in Sociological Research. Page 27

6

PRACTICE TEST

1. The term that stresses the social contexts in which people live and how these contexts influence people's lives is:
   a. The Sociological Perspective
   b. Social Solidarity
   c. The Social Imperative
   d. The Sociological Framework

2. The social event most closely linked to the development of sociology was the:
   a. Great Depression
   b. Industrial Revolution
   c. Discovery of America
   d. Hundred Years War

3. Using objective, systematic observations to test theories is referred to as:
   a. The Positivist Approach
   b. Classical Naturalism
   c. The Scientific Method
   d. Experience

4. The term Karl Marx used to describe the controlling class of capitalists, those who own the means of production, capital, land, and factories was the:
   a. Proletariat
   b. Bourgeoisie
   c. Power Elite
   d. Robber Barons

5. The sociologist who conducted extensive research on varying rates of suicide within a specific country and among different countries was:
   a. Emile Durkheim
   b. Talcott Parsons
   c. Karl Marx
   d. Wright Mills

6. The degree to which people are tied to their social groups is referred to by Emile Durkheim as:
   a. Social Integration
   b. the Social Imperative
   c. the Sociological Imagination
   d. Symbolic Interactionism

7. Max Weber believed the central force in social change was:
   a. religion   b. economics   c. politics   d. the military

8. The sociologist who studied social life in both the United States and Great Britain and documented the results of this research in the book *Society in America* was:
   a. Herbert Spencer
   b. Harriet Martineau
   c. Talcott Parsons
   d. Jane Addams

9. The social reformer who founded Hull House and later won a Nobel Prize was:
   a. Margaret Sanger
   b. Harriet Martineau
   c. Jane Addams
   d. Sue Ellen Butler

10. The first African American to earn a doctorate degree at Harvard University was:
    a. Booker T. Washington
    b. George Washington Carver
    c. Benjamin Anthony Quarles
    d. W.E.B. DuBois

11. The term C. Wright Mills used for the top leaders of business, politics, and the military who, together, comprised an intimate threat to freedoms was:
    a. the Silent Majority
    b. the Middle Class
    c. the Fortune 500 Club
    d. the Power Elite

12. The use of sociology to solve problems is referred to as:
    a. theoretical sociology
    b. pure sociology
    c. applied sociology
    d. positivist sociology

13. In the 1940s the central focus of sociology
    a. shifted from data gathering to social activism.
    b. shifted from social reform to social theory.
    c. shifted from theories developed in America to theories developed in Europe.
    d. shifted from predicting behavior to explaining behavior.

14. The underlying principle of symbolic interactionism is:
    a. how society uses sanctions to control behavior
    b. that behavior is determined by factors beyond one's control
    c. the history of man is a study of class conflict
    d. how one's behavior depends on the way we define ourselves and others

15. When people change their ideas and behavior about an issue, such as divorce, based on a changing image of that issue and what it means is example of:
    a. structural functionalism
    b. symbolic interactionism
    c. neo-conflict perspective
    d. the conflict perspective

16. The sociological perspective that holds the central idea that society is a whole unit, made up of interrelated parts that work together is:
    a. Symbolic Interactionism
    b. Functional Analysis
    c. Classical Naturalism
    d. Conflict Theory

17. An intended outcome or consequence that helps keep society in equilibrium is referred to as being a:
    a. latent function
    b. dysfunction
    c. manifest function
    d. symbolic function

18. What theory was developed by Karl Marx to explain the relationship between the social classes?
    a. social integration theory
    b. functional analysis
    c. ethnomethodology
    d. conflict theory

19. Conflict theory sees the modern increase in divorce rates as
    a. the weakening importance of the role of the family.
    b. a sign that women are making headway in their historical struggle with men.
    c. a change in the symbolic meaning associated with marriage and divorce.
    d. an indication that attorneys now have the greatest influence on the informal legal structure.

20. A statement of what a researcher may expect to find according to predictions based on a theory is a/an:
    a. correlation
    b. operational definition
    c. paradigm
    d. hypothesis

21. When a question is asked of survey respondents and then the respondent is given a list of possible answers, this type of question is called:
    a. a closed ended question
    b. an open-ended question
    c. establishing rapport
    d. participant observation

22. If you were to analyze data that someone else has already collected, you would be doing:
    a. an experiment
    b. participant observation
    c. secondary analysis
    d. survey research

23. A variable that causes a change in another variable is referred to as:
    a. a dependent variable
    b. an independent variable
    c. an operational definition
    d. a secondary analysis

24. Ethics in sociological research
    a. forbids the falsification of results.
    b. condemns plagiarism.
    c. promotes sociologists to protect the anonymity of people who provide information.
    d. all of the above

25. Max Weber's insistence that sociology be value free, focuses on
    a. religious freedom.
    b. sociologists having no individual values of their own.
    c. society's accepting all values without showing favoritism towards a particular value.
    d. objectivity in research.

PRACTICE TEST — ANSWER KEY

1. A (page 2)
2. B (page 3)
3. A (page 3)
4. B (page 4)
5. A (page 5)
6. A (page 5)
7. A (pages 5-6)
8. B (page 6)
9. C (page 7)

10. D (page 7)
11. D (page 8)
12. C (page 8)
13. B (page 8)
14. D (pages 11-12)
15. B (pages 12-13)
16. B (page 13)
17. C (page 13)
18. D (page 15)

19. B (page 15)
20. D (page 18)
21. A (page 22)
22. C (page 25)
23. B (page 25)
24. D (pages 25-26)
25. D (page 27)

CHAPTER 2

CULTURE

KEY TERMS

counterculture: a subculture whose values place its members in opposition to the values of the broader culture

cultural diffusion: the spread of cultural characteristics from one group to another

cultural lag: William Ogburn's term for a situation in which nonmaterial culture lags behind changes in the material culture

cultural leveling: the process by which cultures become similar to one another; especially refers to the process by which western industrial culture is imported and diffused into other cultures

cultural relativism: understanding a people from the framework of their own culture

culture: the languages, beliefs, values, norms, behaviors, and even material objects that are passed from one generation to the next

culture shock: the disorientation that people experience when they come in contact with a fundamentally different culture and can no longer depend on their taken-for-granted assumptions about life

ethnocentrism: the use of one's own culture as a yardstick for judging the ways of other individuals and societies, generally leading to a negative evaluation of their values, norms, and behaviors

folkways: norms that are not strictly enforced

gestures: the ways in which people use their bodies to communicate with one another

ideal culture: the ideal values and norms of a people, the goals held out for them

language: a system of symbols that can be combined in an infinite number of ways to communicate abstract thought

material culture: the material objects that distinguish a group of people, such as their art, buildings, weapons, utensils, machines, hairstyles, clothing, and jewelry

mores: norms strictly enforced because they are thought essential to core values

negative sanction: an expression of disapproval for breaking a norm; ranging from a mild, informal reaction such as a frown to a formal prison sentence, banishment, or death

new technology: a technology introduced into a society that has a significant impact on that society

nonmaterial culture: (also called symbolic culture): a group's ways of thinking (including its beliefs, values, and other assumptions about the world) and doing (its common patterns or behavior, including language and other forms of interaction)

norms: the expectations, or rules of behavior, that develop out of values

pluralistic society: a society made up of many different groups

positive sanction: a reward or positive reaction for following norms, ranging from a smile to a prize

real culture: the norms and values that people actually follow (as opposed to ideal culture)

sanction: an expression of approval or disapproval given to people for upholding or violating norms

Sapir-Whorf hypothesis: Edward Sapir's and Benjamin Whorf's hypothesis that language creates was of thinking and perceiving

subculture: the values and related behaviors of a group that distinguish its members from the larger culture; a world within a world

symbol: something to which people attach meaning and then use to communicate with others

symbolic culture: another term for nonmaterial culture

taboo: a norm so strong that it brings revulsion if it is violated

technology: in its narrow sense, tools; in its broader sense, the skills or procedures necessary to make and use those tools

value cluster: a series of interrelated values that together form a larger whole

value contradiction: values that contradict one another; to follow the one means to come into conflict with the other

values: the standards by which people define what is desirable or undesirable, good or bad, beautiful or ugly

KEY PEOPLE

Robert Edgerton: Edgerton attacks the concept of cultural relativism, suggesting that because some cultures endanger their people's health, happiness, or survival, there would be a scale to evaluate cultures on their *quality of life*.

Douglas Massey: This sociologist has studied what happens in urban areas when immigration rates exceed the speed with which new residents can learn English and the proportion of non-English speakers increases.

William Ogburn: Ogburn coined the term *cultural lag*.

Edward Sapir and Benjamin Whorf: These anthropologists argued that language not only reflects thoughts and perceptions, but that it actually shapes the way a people perceive the world.

JoEllen Shively: Shively researched the reasons why both Anglo and Native American moviegoers identify more with the cowboys than the Indians.

William Sumner: Sumner developed the concept of ethnocentrism.

Robin Williams: He identified twelve core United States values.

Essentials of Sociology
Sixth Edition

Chapter Two:
Culture

Chapter Overview

- ❖ What is Culture?
- ❖ Components of Symbolic Culture
- ❖ Many Cultural Worlds: Subcultures and Countercultures

- ❖ Values in U.S. Society
- ❖ Technology in the Global Village
- ❖ Cultural Lag, Diffusion, and Labeling

Copyright © Allyn & Bacon 2006   2

What is Culture?

❖ Language, Beliefs, Values, Norms,

Behavior Passed from One Generation to

the Next

❖ Material vs. Nonmaterial Cultures

Copyright © Allyn & Bacon 2006   3

Culture and Taken-for-Granted Orientations

❖What is Normal, Natural, or Usual?

❖The Culture Within Us

❖Culture as Lens

❖Culture Shock

❖Ethnocentrism

Copyright © Allyn & Bacon 2006   4

Practicing Cultural Relativism

Culture

❖Understanding Cultures on Their Own Terms

❖"Sick Cultures"

❖Confronting Contrasting Views of Reality

Copyright © Allyn & Bacon 2006   5

Components of Symbolic Culture

Culture

❖Symbol is Something to Which People Attach Meaning

❖Gestures

❖Language

Copyright © Allyn & Bacon 2006   6

Language and Culture

❖Allows Human Experience to Be
Cumulative

❖Provides a Social or Shared Past

❖Provides a Social or Shared Future

❖Allows Shared Perspectives

❖Allows Complex, Shared, Goal Directed
Behavior

7

Language and Perception: Sapir-Whorf

❖Language Has Embedded Within It
Ways of Looking at the World

❖Sapir Whorf Reverses Common Sense

8

Values, Norms, and Sanctions

❖Values- What is Desirable in Life

❖Norms- Expectations or Rules for
Behavior

❖Sanctions- Reaction to Following or
Breaking Norms

❖Positive Sanctions

❖Negative Sanctions

9

Folkways and Mores

❖Folkways- Norms not Strictly Enforced

❖Mores- Core Values. We Insist on

Conformity

Copyright © Allyn & Bacon 2006   10

Subcultures & Countercultures

❖Subculture- A World Within the

Dominant Culture

❖Countercultures- Groups With Norms

and Values at Odds with the Dominant

Culture

Copyright © Allyn & Bacon 2006   11

Values in U.S. Society

Achievement and Success	Progress	Equality
Individualism	Material Comfort	Racism and Group Superiority
Activity and Work	Humanitarianism	Education
Efficiency and Practicality	Freedom	Religiosity
Science and Technology	Democracy	Romantic Love

Copyright © Allyn & Bacon 2006   12

Values in U.S. Society

❖Achievement and Success

❖Individualism

❖Activity and Work

❖Efficiency and Practicality

❖Science and Technology

13

Values in U.S. Society

❖Progress

❖Material Comfort

❖Humanitarianism

❖Freedom

❖Democracy

14

Values in U.S. Society

❖Equality

❖Racism and Group
 Superiority

❖Education

❖Religiosity

❖Romantic Love

15

Value Clusters and Contradictions

❖ Value Clusters - Series of
  Interrelated Values

❖ Values Contradictions - Values
  that Contradict One Another

16

Value Contradictions and Social Change

"It is precisely at the point of value

contradictions, then, that one can

see a major force for social change

in a society"

17

Emerging Values

❖Leisure

❖Self fulfillment

❖Physical Fitness

❖Youthfulness

❖Concern for the
  Environment

18

Values and Culture

❖Culture Wars: When Values Clash

❖Value as Blinders

❖"Ideal" vs. "Real" Culture

19

Technology in the Global Village

❖The New Technology- New Tools

❖Cultural Lag and Cultural Change

❖Technology and Cultural Leveling

20

Figure 2.1 Gesture to Indicate Height, Southern Mexico, Page 37.

Copyright © Allyn & Bacon 2006

2

PRACTICE TEST

1. Which of the following characteristics are indicative of culture?
   a.   The language spoken by a people.   c. The values and norms of a people.
   b.   The beliefs of a people.   d. All of the above

2. Things such as jewelry, art, hairstyle, and clothing are referred to as:
   a.   material culture   c. cognitive culture
   b.   nonmaterial culture   d. technological culture

3. A group's way of thinking and common patterns of behavior are referred to as:
   a.   material culture   c. cognitive culture
   b.   nonmaterial culture   d. technology

4. Which of the following *is not* an example of nonmaterial culture?
   a.   Language   b. Gestures   c. Art   d. Symbols

5. Disorientation experienced by being in a situation where an individual's sense of nonmaterial culture is insufficient to understand a specific situation is referred to as:
   a.   culture shock   c. ethnocentrism
   b.   cultural relativism   d. cultural lag

6. Trying to understand a culture in its own terms and not one's own is referred to as:
   a.   ethnocentrism   c. relativist fallacy
   b.   cultural relativism   d. cultural shock

7. Symbolic culture is a term sometimes used interchangeably with the term:
   a.   cognitive culture   c. material culture
   b.   language as culture   d. nonmaterial culture

8. A system of symbols that can be strung together in an infinite number of ways for the purpose of communicating abstract thought defines:
   a.   symbols   b. sanctions   c. language   d. emotions

9. _____ are considered as useful shorthand ways to convey messages without using words.
   a.   Norms   b. Folkways   c. Gestures   d. Mores

10. Written gestures for expressing yourself online are commonly known as:
    a.   symbols   c.   icons
    b.   emoticons   d.   technology

11. The concept that language determines consciousness and shapes one's perception of objects and events is the:
    a.   Korsikoff Syndrome   c. Malthus Theorem
    b.   Thomas Theorem   d. Sapir-Whorf Hypothesis

12. The concept that describes what people find desirable in life, what is good and bad, is:
    a.   values   b. beliefs   c. norms   d. folkways

13. The reaction of society directed at an individual for following or breaking norms is referred to as a/an:
    a.   compensation   b. construct   c. sanction   d. variable

14. Serving turkey for Thanksgiving dinner is an example of a
    a.   vice.   c.   core value.
    b.   taboo.   d.   folkway.

15. A monetary fine, harsh words, or a raised fist is an example of:
    a.   negative sanction   c. taboo
    b.   cultural universal   d. positive sanction

16. Of the following situations, which one is most clearly the violation of a more?
    a.   Armed robbery   c. Divorce
    b.   Premarital sex   d. Incest

17. What is a counterculture?
    a.   a group which has its own values and norms but identifies with the main culture
    b.   a group which has values in opposition to the dominant culture
    c.   any sub-unit of the main culture
    d.   a group with the same values as the dominant culture

18. A value-cluster of four interrelated core values is emerging in the United States. Which one of the following is NOT part of this emerging value cluster?
    a.   Leisure   c. Physical fitness
    b.   Self-fulfillment   d. Appreciation of elders

19. Sociologists use the term _____ to refer to a group's values and norms that they actually follow.
    a.   real culture   c. ideal culture
    b.   cultural universal   d. high culture

20. The term _____ refers to the emerging advancements in science, tools, and the skills to use them that have a significant impact on social life.
    a.   new technology   c. global technology
    b.   value cluster   d. core values

21. The distinguishing factor between *technology* and *new technology* is that:
    a.   technology is developed by less advanced cultures than new technology.
    b.   technology fails to change nonmaterial culture whereas new technology does.
    c.   new technologies have a greater impact on social life than technology.
    d.   there is no difference in technology and new technology other than the name.

22. Who coined the term cultural lag?
    a.   William Ogburn   c.   Talcott Parsons
    b.   Max Weber   d.   August Comte

23. Which term refers to the custom of maintaining a nine-month school year in the U.S. even though this custom no longer matches the current technology?
    a.   cultural diffusion   c. cultural hindrance
    b.   cultural leveling   d. cultural lag

24. When nations throughout the world begin to share fads and fashions, they are exhibiting:
    a.   cultural degradation   c. cultural relativism
    b.   cultural leveling   d. ethnocentrism

25. Mexican piñatas often depict Mickey Mouse or Fred Flintstone. This is an example of
    a.   symbolic culture.   c. cultural leveling.
    b.   cultural lag.   d. cultural relativism.

PRACTICE TEST — ANSWER KEY

1. D (page 32)
2. A (page 32)
3. B (page 33)
4. C (page 33)
5. A (page 33)
6. B (page 34)
7. D (page 36)
8. C (page 37)
9. C (page 37)

10. B (page 39)
11. D (page 41)
12. A (page 42)
13. C (page 42)
14. D (page 42)
15. A (page 42)
16. A (page 42)
17. B (page 43)
18. D (page 48)

19. A (page 49)
20. A (page 50)
21. C (page 50)
22. A (page 50)
23. D (page 50)
24. B (page 51)
25. C (page 51)

CHAPTER 3

SOCIALIZATION

KEY TERMS

agents of socialization: people and groups that influence our self-concept, emotions, attitudes, and behavior

anticipatory socialization: as we anticipate future roles, we learn aspects of them now (p. 70)

degradation ceremony: a term coined by Harold Garfinkel to describe rituals that are designed to strip an individual of his or her identity as a group member; for example, a court martial or the defrocking of a priest

ego: Freud's term for a balancing force between the id and the demands of society (p. 64)

gender socialization: the ways in which society sets children onto different courses in life because they are male or female

generalized other: taking the role of a larger number of people

id: Freud's term for the individual's inborn basic drives

life course: the stages of our life as we go from birth to death

looking-glass self: a term coined by Charles Horton Cooley to refer to the process by which our self develops through internalizing other's reactions to us

mass media: forms of communication directed to large audiences

peer group: a group of individuals of roughly the same age who are linked by common interests

resocialization: the process of learning new norms, values, attitudes, and behaviors

self: the concept, unique to humans, of being able to see ourselves "from the outside"; our internalized perception of how others see us

significant other: an individual who significantly influences someone else's life

social environment: the entire human environment, including direct contact with others

socialization: the process by which people learn the characteristics of their group—the attitudes, values, and actions thought appropriate for them

superego: Freud's term for the conscience, which consists of the internalized norms and values of our social groups

taking the role of the other: putting oneself in someone else's shoes; understanding how someone else feels and thinks and thus anticipates how that person will act

total institution: a place in which people are cut off from the rest of society and are almost totally controlled by the officials who run the place

KEY PEOPLE

Patricia and Peter Adler: These sociologists have documented how peer groups socialize children into gender-appropriate behavior.

Philippe Ariés: Ariés studied paintings from the Middle Ages to learn more about past notions of childhood.

Charles H. Cooley: Cooley studied the development of the self, coining the term the *looking-glass self.*

Sigmund Freud: Freud developed a theory of personality development that took into consideration inborn drives (id), the internalized norms and values of one's society (superego), and the individual's ability to balance the two competing forces (ego).

Erving Goffman: Goffman studied the process of resocialization with total institutions.

Susan Goldberg and Michael Lewis: Two psychologists studied how parents' unconscious expectations about gender behavior are communicated to their young children.

Harry and Margaret Harlow: These psychologists studied the behavior of monkeys raised in isolation and found that the length of time they were in isolation affected their ability to overcome the effects of isolation.

Kenneth Keniston: Keniston noted that industrial societies seem to be adding a period of prolonged youth to the life course, in which adult responsibilities are postponed.

Melvin Kohn: Kohn has done extensive research on the social class differences in child-rearing patterns.

George Herbert Mead: Mead emphasized the importance of play in the development of self-esteem in men.

Jean Piaget: Piaget studied the development of reasoning skills in children.

H.M. Skeels and H.B. Dye: These two psychologists studied the impact that close social interaction had on the social and intellectual development of institutionalized children.

Essentials of Sociology
Sixth Edition

Chapter Three:
Socialization

The multimedia product and its contents are protected under copyright law. The following are prohibited by law: any public performance or display, including transmission of any image over a network; preparation of any derivative work, including the extraction, in whole or in part, of any images; any rental, lease, or lending of the program.

Chapter Overview

❖ What is Human Nature?

❖ Socialization into the Self, Mind, and Emotions

❖ Socialization into Gender

❖ Agents of Socialization

❖ Resocialization

❖ Socialization through the Life Course

❖ Are We Prisoners of Socialization?

Copyright © Allyn & Bacon 2006   2

What is Human Nature?

❖ Nature vs. Nurture

❖ Isolated Children

❖ Institutionalized Children

❖ Deprived Animals

Copyright © Allyn & Bacon 2006   3

In Sum…

…Society Makes Us Human

4

Socialization into the Self, Mind, and Emotions

❖Cooley and the Looking Glass Self

  ❖We Imagine How We Appear to Others

  ❖We Interpret Others' Reactions

  ❖We Develop a Self-Concept

Socialization into the Self, Mind, and Emotions

❖Children Learn to Take the Role of Others

❖Mead and Role Taking

  ❖Imitation

  ❖Play

  ❖Games

❖Self and Mind are Social Products

6

Socialization into the Self, Mind, and Emotions

❖Piaget and the Development of

Reasoning

- ❖Sensorimotor Stage
- ❖Preopertional Stage
- ❖Concrete Operational Stage
- ❖Formal Operational Stage

Copyright © Allyn & Bacon 2006   7

Global Aspects of the Self and Reasoning

- ❖ Stages of Reasoning Universal, Age of Entry

  Not Necessarily Universal

- ❖ Stages not As Distinct as Previously Thought

- ❖ Basic Structure of Reasoning Development is

  Concrete to Abstract

Copyright © Allyn & Bacon 2006   8

Freud and the Development of Personality

- ❖ Founded Psychoanalysis
- ❖ Personality Consists of Three Elements
    - ❖The Id
    - ❖The Ego
    - ❖The Superego
- ❖ However, It Denies Central Principle of

  Sociology

Copyright © Allyn & Bacon 2006   9

Socialization and Emotions

❖Global Emotions

❖Expressing Emotions

❖What We Feel

❖Research Needed

❖The Self and Emotions as Social Control

Society Within Us

10

Socialization into Gender

❖Gender Messages in the Family

❖The Peer Group

❖Gender Messages in the Mass Media

   ❖Television and Movies

   ❖Video Games

Agents of Socialization

❖The Family

❖The Neighborhood

❖Religion

❖Day Care

12

Agents of Socialization

❖The School and Peer Groups

❖The Workplace

❖Resocialization

❖Total Institutions

Socialization Through Life

❖Childhood- Birth to ~12 yrs

❖Adolescence- 13 to 17 yrs

❖Young Adulthood- 18 to 29 yrs

14

Socialization Through Life

❖The Middle Years- 30 to 65 yrs

　❖Early Middle Years - 30 to 45 yrs

　❖Later Middle Years - 50 to 65 yrs

❖The Older Years- ~65 yrs on

15

Are We Prisoners of Socialization?

❖ Sociologists Do Not Think So

❖ Socialization is Powerful, but the Self is Dynamic

❖ Individuals Are Actively Involved in the Construction of the Self

Copyright © Allyn & Bacon 2006   16

Essentials of Sociology

Sixth Edition

Chapter Three:
Socialization

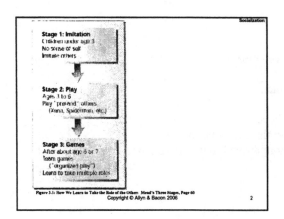

Stage 1: Imitation
Children under age 3
No sense of self
Imitate others

Stage 2: Play
Ages 3 to 6
Play "pretend" others
(Xena, Spiderman, etc.)

Stage 3: Games
After about age 6 or 7
Team games
("organized play")
Learn to take multiple roles

Figure 3.1: How We Learn to Take the Role of the Other: Mead's Three Stages, Page 60
Copyright © Allyn & Bacon 2006

2

PRACTICE TEST

1. In the "nature vs. nurture" debate, "nature" refers to:
   a. heredity
   b. personality
   c. the environment
   d. intellect

2. In the "nature vs. nurture" debate, "nurture" refers to:
   a. heredity
   b. the social environment
   c. an individual's IQ
   d. an individual's genealogy

3. Which of the following influences or traits best prepares a person to be a contributing member of human society?
   a. a superior IQ
   b. a strong personal physique
   c. contact with other humans
   d. basic instincts inherited from family

4. The case of Jack and Oskar teaches us:
   a. the far reaching effects of the environment
   b. how biology overrides social experiences
   c. the importance of genetic heredity
   d. to dismiss the role of society in personal development

5. We can conclude from the Harlow experiment that:
   a. humans are very similar to monkeys
   b. instinct is the only motivating force in monkeys
   c. monkeys lack the ability to go through a socialization process
   d. the longer the monkeys were isolated the more difficult it was for them to adjust to normal monkey life

6. The Looking Glass Self concept was the creation of:
   a. George Herbert Mead
   b. Charles Horton Cooley
   c. Jean Piaget
   d. Sigmund Freud

7. The Looking Glass Self is based on the premise that we develop a sense of self from:
   a. interaction with others
   b. by the type of movies and television we watch
   c. our genetic makeup
   d. our unconscious personality

8. According to Mead, _____ refers to our perception of how people as a whole think of us.
   a. significant others
   b. reference groups
   c. generalized others
   d. out-groups

9. In Mead's theory of development, the "I" is the:
   a. self we are aware of
   b. self as social object
   c. outwardly directed part of the self
   d. spontaneous, creative part of the self

10. From the age of about 3 to 6, children pretend to take the role of specific people. According to Mead, this stage is called:
    a. imitation
    b. play
    c. game
    d. reference group

11. Jean Piaget focused on studying how children develop
    a. the ability to understand language.
    b. the ability to read.
    c. the ability to perform mathematical equations.
    d. the ability to reason.

12. The first stage proposed by Piaget in which the child's understanding is limited to direct contact with the environment, such as touching, seeing, and listening is called the:
    a. preoperational stage
    b. sensorimotor stage
    c. concrete operational stage
    d. early development stage

13. What term does Sigmund Freud use to represent the "culture within us," the norms and values we have internalized for our social groups?
    a. Id
    b. Superego
    c. Eros
    d. Ego

14. People and groups that influence our self concept, emotions, attitudes, and behavior are referred to as:
    a. components of personality
    b. generalized others
    c. agents of socialization
    d. instrumental relationships

15. According to the research of Melvin Kohn, working-class parents are most concerned with the development of which trait by their children?
    a. independence
    b. creativity
    c. conformity
    d. intellectual superiority

16. According to a study by the National Institute of Child Health and Human Development, the more time a child spends in day care:
    a. the more cooperative the child is in the home and at day care
    b. the stronger the bond between the child and their mother
    c. the fewer behavior problems the child exhibits at home
    d. the weaker the bond between the child and their mother

17. During a typical week, _____ Americans attend a religious service.
    a. one in four
    b. two in five
    c. half of all
    d. all

18. The concept that addresses learning to play a role before actually entering it is:
    a. anticipatory socialization
    b. resocialization
    c. ethnomethodology
    d. functional analysis

19. Which quality is less accurate when describing the total institution?
    a. Total institutions are a powerful agent of socialization.
    b. People in total institutions are in a place where they are cut off from the rest of society.
    c. Although isolated, members of a total institution retain their individuality and dignity.
    d. Boot camps, prisons, and convents are examples of total institutions.

20. The process of learning new norms, values, attitudes, and behaviors is
    a. degradation.
    b. resocialization.
    c. leveling.
    d. anticipatory socialization.

21. An attempt to strip a person of his or her identity, so as to remake a new identity
    a. is exemplified by one's being allowed to keep their personal identity kit.
    b. applies to all institutions of society.
    c. is an example of a positive sanction.
    d. is part of a degradation ceremony.

22. Stages we experience from birth to death are called
    a. the life course.
    b. social locations.
    c. statuses.
    d. socialization.

23. Which statement is *least true* of the life course?
    a. It includes a series of stages from birth to death.
    b. Each stage a person passes through affects their behavior and orientation.
    c. Everyone's life course will differ based upon his or her social location.
    d. The life course is basically the same for males and females of the same age and social location.

24. Which statement best describes adolescence?
    a. Human nature makes this a time filled with inner turmoil.
    b. Contemporary society, not biology, makes this a time of inner turmoil.
    c. In postindustrial societies children are treated as adults.
    d. It is a natural age division separating innocence from responsibility.

25. Which statement best describes socialization?
    a. Sociologists view most behavior as being a robotic response to life.
    b. People cannot help what they do because all behavior is linked to socializing agents.
    c. Behavior is fairly predictable if one can isolate a child and expose them to only certain agents of socialization.
    d. Humans have the power to change their behavior and concept of self by purposely exposing themselves to different social frameworks.

PRACTICE TEST — ANSWER KEY

1. A (page 56)
2. B (page 56)
3. C (page 56)
4. A (page 57)
5. D (pages 58-59)
6. B (page 59)
7. A (pages 59-60)
8. C (page 60)
9. D (page 61)

10. B (page 60-61)
11. D (page 61)
12. B (page 61)
13. B (page 62)
14. C (page 68)
15. C (page 68)
16. D (page 68-69)
17. B (page 68)
18. A (page 69)

19. C (page 71)
20. B (page 71)
21. D (page 71)
22. A (page 71)
23. D (page 71)
24. B (page 73-74)
25. D (page 75)

CHAPTER 4

SOCIAL STRUCTURE AND SOCIAL INTERACTION

KEY TERMS

achieved statuses: positions that are earned, accomplished, or that involve at least some effort or activity on the individual's part.

ascribed statuses: positions an individual either inherits at birth or receives involuntarily later in life

background assumptions: deeply embedded common understandings (basic rules or *codes*) concerning our view of the world and how people ought to act

division of labor: how work is divided among the members of a group

dramaturgy: an approach, pioneered by Erving Goffman, analyzing social life in terms of drama and the stage

ethnomethodology: the study of how people use background assumptions to make sense of life

face-saving behavior: techniques people use to salvage a performance that is going sour

Gemeinschaft: a type of society in which life is intimate; a community in which everyone knows everyone else and people share a sense of togetherness

Gesellschaft: a type of society dominated by impersonal relationships, individual accomplishments, and self-interest

group: people who regularly and consciously interact with one another; in a general sense, people who have something in common and who believe that what they have in common is significant

horticultural society: a society based on the cultivation of plants by the use of hand tools

hunting and gathering society: a society dependent on hunting and gathering for survival

impression management: the term used by Erving Goffman to describe people's efforts to control the impressions that others receive of them

Industrial Revolution: the third social revolution; it occurred when machines powered by fuels replaced most animal and human power

macrosociology: analysis of social life that focuses on broad features of social structure, such as social class and the relationships of groups to one another; an approach usually used by functionalist and conflict theorists

master status: a status that cuts across the other statuses that an individual occupies

mechanical solidarity: Durkheim's term for the unity or shared consciousness that comes from being involved in similar occupations or activities

microsociology: analysis of social life that focuses on social interaction; an approach usually used by symbolic interactionists

organic solidarity: Durkheim's term for the interdependence that results from people needing the skills, work and products of one another; the solidarity based on the division of labor

pastoral society: a society based on the pasturing of animals

role: the behaviors, obligations, and privileges attached to a status

role conflict: conflict that someone feels because the expectations attached to one role are incompatible with the expectations of another role

role strain: conflicts that someone feels *within* a role

social class: a large number of people who have similar amounts of income and education and who work at jobs that are roughly comparable in prestige

social cohesion: the degree to which members of a group or a society feel united by shared values and other social bonds

social construction of reality: the use of background assumptions and life experiences to define what is real

social institution: the organized, usual, or standard ways by which society meets its basic needs

social interaction: what people do when they are in one another's presence; this can be a virtual presence, such as the telephone or the Internet

social structure: the relationship of people and groups to one another

society: a group of people who share a culture and a territory

status: the position that someone occupies; one's social ranking

status inconsistency: a contradiction or mismatch between statuses; a condition in which a person ranks high on some dimensions of social class and low on others

status set: all the statuses or positions that an individual occupies

status symbols: items used to identify a status

teamwork: the collaboration of two or more persons who, interested in the success of a performance, manage impressions jointly

Thomas theorem: basically, that people live in socially constructed world; that is, people jointly build their own realities; as summarized by William I. Thomas's statement: "If people define situations as real, they are real in their consequences."

KEY PEOPLE

William Chambliss: Chambliss used macro and microsociology to study high school gangs and found that social structure and interaction explained the patterns of behavior in these groups. groups.

Emile Durkheim: Durkheim identified mechanical and organic solidarity as the keys to social cohesion.

Harold Garfinkel: Garfinkel is the founder of ethnomethodology; he conducted experiments in order to uncover people's background assumptions.

Erving Goffman: Goffman developed dramaturgy, the perspective within symbolic interactionism that views social life as a drama on the stage.

Edward Hall: This anthropologist found that personal space varied from one culture to another and that North Americans use four different *distance zones*.

W. I. Thomas: This sociologist was known for his statement, "If people define situations as real, they are real in their consequences."

Ferdinand Tönnies: Tönnies analyzed different types of societies that existed before and after industrialization. He used the terms *Gemeinschaft* and *Gesellschaft* to describe the two types of societies.

Essentials of Sociology

Sixth Edition

James M. Henslin

**Chapter Four: Social Structure
and Social Interaction**

This multimedia product and its contents are protected under copyright law. The following are prohibited by law:
any public performance or display, including transmission of any image over a network;
preparation of any derivative work, including the extraction, in whole or in part, of any images;
any rental, lease, or lending of the program.

Chapter Overview

- ❖ Levels of Sociological Analysis
- ❖ The Macrosociological Perspective:
  Social Structure
- ❖ The Microsociological Perspective:
  Social Interaction in Everyday Life
- ❖ The Need for Both Macrosociology
  and Microsociology

Copyright © Allyn & Bacon 2006

2

Levels of Sociological Analysis

- ❖Macrosociology
  - ❖Large-Scale Features of Social Life
- ❖Microsociology
  - ❖Focus on Social Interaction

Copyright © Allyn & Bacon 2006

3

48

The Macrosociological Perspective: Social Structure

❖Sociological Significance of Social Structure

  ❖Guides Our Behavior

  ❖Behavior Decided by Location in Social Structure

❖Culture

  ❖Group's Language, Beliefs, Values, Behaviors, Gestures

  ❖Material Objects

4

The Macrosociological Perspective

❖ Need to Understand Social Locations People Hold in Life

❖ Social Class Divides People by…

  ❖Income

  ❖Education

  ❖Occupational Prestige

5

Social Class: Income, education occupational presorge

The Macrosociological Perspective

❖Social Status

  ❖Ascribed

  ❖Achieved

  ❖Status Symbols

  ❖Master Statuses

  ❖Status Inconsistency

6

Social status:
- ascribed: being another
- achieved
- status symbols: represent
- Master Statuses
- Status Inconsistency: teachers dating young teenagers

The Macrosociological Perspective

❖ Roles - Behaviors, Obligations, Privileges Attached to a Status

❖ Status vs. Role

  ❖You Occupy a Status

  ❖You Play a Role

Copyright © Allyn & Bacon 2006   7

Status vs. Role
- You occupy a status
- You play a role

Groups & Social Institutions

❖ Groups - People Who Regularly and Consciously Interact

❖ Social Institutions - Means Developed by Societies to Meet Basic Needs

Copyright © Allyn & Bacon 2006   8

Societies and Their Transformations

❖ Society - People Who Share and Culture and Territory

❖ Society Evolved Through Stages:

  ❖Hunting and Gathering

  ❖Pastoral and Horticultural

  ❖Agricultural

  ❖Industrial

  ❖Post-Industrial

Copyright © Allyn & Bacon 2006

Society evolved through stages
- Hunting and Gathering
- Pastoral and
- agricultural
- industrialize

50

Bioeconomic Society

❖ Economy that Centers on
Application of Genetics

❖ Apply to Medicines and Food

❖ Information Transmission
Extended to Smell, Taste, and
Touch

Copyright © Allyn & Bacon 2006   10

What Holds Society Together?

❖ Mechanical Solidarity

❖ Organic Solidarity

❖ Gemeinschaft and Gesellschaft

Copyright © Allyn & Bacon 2006   11

Mechanical solidarity - people
were held together for
the same types of organic
solidarity -
Gemeinschaft and gesellschaft

Microsociological Perspective: Social Interaction in Everyday Life

Copyright © Allyn & Bacon 2006   12

51

Social Interaction in Everyday Life

❖ Stereotypes

❖ Personal Space
   ❖ Intimate
   ❖ Personal
   ❖ Social
   ❖ Public

+ Cross-Cultural Conversation and Interaction Style

Copyright © Allyn & Bacon 2006   13

Intimate: 0 in

Personal:

Social: 4 ft 12

Public:

Dramaturgy:
The Presentation of Self in Everyday Life

❖ Erving Goffman
   ❖ Dramaturgy
   ❖ Impression Management
   ❖ Front and Back Stages
   ❖ Role Conflict
   ❖ Role Strain Between and Within Roles
   ❖ Teamwork and Face-Saving Behavior

Copyright © Allyn & Bacon 2006   14

Dramaturgy - life is like a
play. Front stage - fill a
seat Back
Impression management -
maintaining the level people
used
want to seeing you in.
role strain - internal conflict
face saving

Ethnomethodology:
Uncovering Background Assumptions

❖ The Study of How People Do Things

❖ Background Assumptions

❖ Harold Garfinkle's Experiments

Copyright © Allyn & Bacon 2006   15

Social Construction of Reality

❖ Definition of the Situation
   - Thomas Theorem

❖ Objective Reality vs.
   Subjective Interpretation

❖ Gynecological
   Examinations

16

Social Construction of Reality

❖ Definition of the Situation -
   Thomas Theorem

❖ Objective Reality vs. Subjective
   Interpretation

❖ Gynecological Examinations

❖ Social Interaction on the Internet

17

Need for Macrosociology and Microsociology

❖ Understanding Incomplete without Both

❖ Consider the Example of Groups Studied

   by William Chambliss

18

Essentials of Sociology
Sixth Edition

**Chapter Four: Social Structure
and Social Interaction**

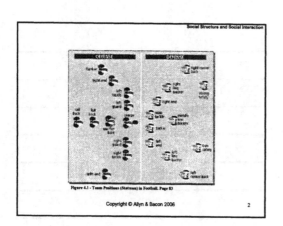

Figure 4.1 - Team Positions (Statuses) in Football, Page 83

2

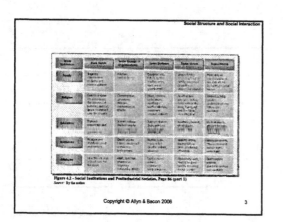

Figure 4.2 - Social Institutions and Postindustrial Societies, Page 86 (part 1)
Source: By the author

3

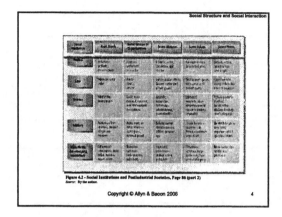

Social Structure and Social Interaction

Figure 4.2 - Social Institutions and Postindustrial Societies, Page 86 (part 2)
Source: By the author.

Copyright © Allyn & Bacon 2006   4

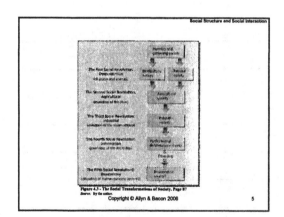

Social Structure and Social Interaction

Figure 4.3 - The Social Transformations of Society, Page 87
Source: By the author.

Copyright © Allyn & Bacon 2006   5

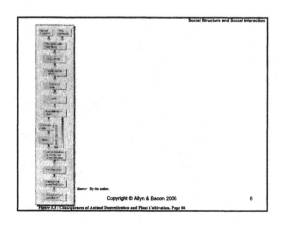

Social Structure and Social Interaction

Source: By the author.

Copyright © Allyn & Bacon 2006   6

Figure 4.4 - Consequences of Animal Domestication and Plant Cultivation, Page 86

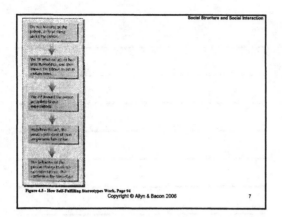

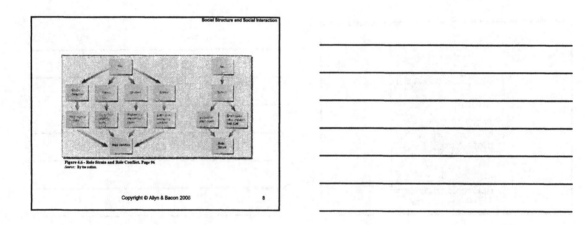

PRACTICE TEST

1. Placing the focus of analysis on the broad features of society such as social class and group interaction is referred to as:
   a. Macrosociology
   b. Microsociology
   c. Functional Analysis
   d. Structural Functionalism

2. Which of the following is *not* a macrosociological approach?
   a. Structural Functionalism
   b. Symbolic Interactionism
   c. the Conflict Perspective
   d. the Neo-Conflict Perspective

3. In microsociology, the emphasis is placed upon:
   a. social interaction
   b. the structure of society
   c. race and ethnic relations
   d. social stratification

4. The typical patterns of a group, such as its usual relationship between men and women, that guides our behavior is referred to as:
   a. social stratification
   b. social structure
   c. social class
   d. social location

5. To a sociologist the term "status" means
   a. a person's occupational prestige level.
   b. a person's position in a society or social group.
   c. a social group's prestige level.
   d. a social group's position in society.

6. Social class is based upon all of the following except:
   a. income
   b. education
   c. occupational prestige
   d. race or ethnic identity

7. The position that an individual occupies in society is referred to as:
   a. role
   b. identity
   c. status
   d. position

8. Of the following, which one *is not* an ascribed status?
   a. divorce
   b. age
   c. race
   d. ethnicity

9. Becoming a college graduate is an
   a. ascribed status
   b. achieved status
   c. status symbol
   d. master status

10. A mismatch between statuses such as a fourteen year-old college student or a 40 year-old married woman dating a 19 year-old sophomore is referred to as:
    a. role conflict
    b. status inconsistency
    c. status set
    d. role strain

11. The behaviors, obligations, and privileges attached to a status are called
    a. status symbols.
    b. master status indicators.
    c. roles.
    d. limitations.

12. The organized ways a society meets its basic needs are called
   a. social institutions.
   c. groups.
   b. roles.
   d. status assignments.

13. The most egalitarian of all societies is the:
   a. agrarian society
   c. pastoral society
   b. horticultural society
   d. hunting and gathering society

14. The _____ is to the agrarian society as the _____ is to the industrial society.
   a. plow/microchip
   c. plow/steam engine
   b. steam engine/microchip
   d. plow/word processor

15. Social inequality became a fundamental feature of social life during which type of society?
   a. Hunting and gathering society
   c. Industrial society
   b. Agricultural society
   d. Postindustrial society

16. The emerging bioeconomic society can be traced to the:
   a. invention of the computer chip
   b. identification of the double-helix structure of DNA
   c. establishment of a new world order
   d. discovery of the A1 and B2 genes

17. As societies get larger, their _____ (how they divide up work) becomes more specialized.
   a. Mechnical solidarity
   c. Division of labor
   b. Gemeinschaft
   d. Bioeconomic society

18. The Amish in the United States represent an example of
   a. organic solidarity.
   b. Gesellschaft.
   c. Gemeinschaft.
   d. a deviant subculture that is not legally protected in our society.

19. Referring to social life as a drama or a stage play describes:
   a. dramaturgy
   c. phenomenonology
   b. ethnomethodology
   d. physiognomy

20. Patti Sue is preparing for her first day of class. Her sociology professor has a reputation for being demanding and a strict grader. She dresses conservatively, reads the first two chapters of the text before class, takes good notes, arrives in class five minutes early, and sits in the front row. Patti Sue is practicing:
   a. role strain
   c. social cohesion
   b. status inconsistency
   d. impression management

21. When two or more people work together to make certain a performance goes off as planned, it is referred to as:
   a. role strain
   c. social cohesion
   b. teamwork
   d. competition

22. A person's ideas about the way life is and the way things ought to work is referred to as:
   a. background assumptions
   c. institutional discrimination
   b. ethnocentrism
   d. secondary analysis

23. Who is the founder of ethnomethodology?
    a. Emile Durkheim
    b. Karl Marx
    c. Harold Garfinkel
    d. W.I. Thomas

24. "If people believe situations are real, they are real in their consequences" is also known as the:
    a. Sapir-Whorf Hypothesis
    b. Thomas Theorem
    c. Looking Glass Self
    d. Social Imperative

25. In the "Saints and "Rednecks" passage, William Chambliss demonstrated the importance of
    _____ and _____ to understand what happened to the two groups.
    a. race/ethnicity
    b. gender socialization/social cohesion
    c. social class/personal wealth
    d. social structure/social interaction

PRACTICE TEST — ANSWER KEY

1. A (page 80)
2. B (page 80)
3. A (page 80)
4. B (page 81)
5. B (page 82)
6. D (page 82)
7. C (page 82)
8. A (page 82)
9. B (page 82)

10. B (page 84)
11. C (page 84)
12. A (page 85)
13. D (page 87)
14. C (page 89)
15. B (page 87)
16. B (page 89)
17. C (page 91)
18. C (page 91)

19. A (page 95)
20. D (page 95)
21. B (page 96)
22. A (page 97)
23. C (page 97)
24. B (page 97)
25. D (page 101)

CHAPTER 5

SOCIAL GROUPS AND FORMAL ORGANIZATIONS

KEY TERMS

aggregate: people who temporarily share the same physical space but do not see themselves as belonging together

alienation: Marx's term for the experience of being cut off from the product of one's labor, which results in a sense of powerlessness and normlessness

authoritarian leader: a leader who leads by giving orders

bureaucracies: formal organizations with a hierarchy of authority, a clear division of labor, impersonality of positions, and emphasis on written rules, communications, and records

category: people who have similar characteristics

clique: within a larger group, a cluster of people who choose to interact with one another; and internal faction

coalition: the alignment of some members of a group against others

corporate culture: the orientations that characterize corporate work settings

dyad: the smallest possible group, consisting of two persons

electronic community: people who more or less regularly interact with one another on the Internet

expressive leader: an individual who increases harmony and minimizes conflict in a group; also known as a socioemotional leader

goal displacement: a process in which a goal is displaced by another, such as when an organization adopts new goals

group: people who think of themselves as belonging together and who interact with one another

group dynamics: the ways in which individuals affect groups and the ways in which groups influence individuals

groupthink: Irving Janis's term for a narrowing of thought by a group; of people, leading to the perception that there is only one correct answer; in groupthink the suggestion of alternatives becomes a sign of disloyalty

in-groups: groups toward which one feels loyalty

instrumental leader: an individual who tries to keep the group moving toward its goals; also known as a task-oriented leader

the iron law of oligarchy: Robert Michels's term for the tendency of formal organizations to be dominated by a small, self-perpetuating elite.

Laissez-faire leader: an individual who leads by being highly permissive

Leader: someone who influences other people

Leadership styles: ways in which people express their leadership

Networking: the process of consciously using or cultivating networks for some gain

Out-groups: groups toward which one feels antagonisms

primary group: a group characterized by intimate, long-term, face-to face association and cooperation

rationalization of society: the increasing influence of bureaucracies in society, which makes the *bottom line* of results dominant in social life

reference group: Herbert Hyman's term for a group whose standards we consider as we evaluate ourselves

secondary group: compared with a primary group, a larger, relatively temporary, more anonymous, formal, and impersonal group based on some interest or activity

small group: a group small enough for everyone to interact directly with all the other members

social networks: the social ties radiating outward from the self, that link people together

triad: a group made up of volunteers who organize on the basis of some mutual interest; the Girl Scouts, Baptists, and Alcoholics Anonymous are examples

KEY PEOPLE

George Arquitt and Elaine Fox: These sociologists studied local posts of the VFW and found three types of members and evidence of the iron law of oligarchy

Solomon Asch: Asch is famour for his research on conformity to group pressure.

Charles H. Cooley: It was Cooley who noted the central role of primary groups in the development of one's sense of self.

John Darley and Bibb Latane: These researchers investigated what impact the size of the group has on individual members' attitudes and behaviors. They found that as the group grew in size, individuals' sense of responsibility diminished, their interactions became more formal, and the larger group tends to break down into small ones.

Lloyd Howells and Selwyn Becker: These social psychologists found that factors such as location within a group underlie people's choices of leaders.

Irving Janis: Janis coined the term *groupthink* to refer to the tunnel vision that a group of people sometimes develop.

Rosabeth Moss Kanter: Kanter studied the *invisible* corporate culture for the most part continually reproduces itself by promoting those workers who fit the elite's stereotypical views.

Ronald Lippitt and Ralph White: These social psychologists carried out a class study on leadership styles and found that the style of leadership affected the behavior of group members.

Robert K. Merton: Merton observed that the traits of in-groups become viewed as virtues, while those same traits in out-groups are seen as vices.

Robert Michels: Michels first used the term "the iron law of oligarchy" to describe the tendency for the leaders of an organization to become entrenched.

Stanley Milgram: Milgram's research has contributed greatly to sociological knowledge of group life. He did research on social networks as well as individual conformity to group pressure.

George Ritzer: Ritzer coined the term the *McDonaldization* of society to describe the increasing rationalization of modern social life.

Georg Simmel: This early sociologist was one of the first to note the significance of group size; he used the terms dyad and triad to describe small groups.

Max Weber: Weber studied the rationalization of society but investigating the link between Protestantism and capitalism and identifying the characteristics of bureaucracy.

Essentials of Sociology
Sixth Edition

Chapter Five: Social Groups
and Formal Organizations

This multimedia product and its contents are protected under copyright law. The following are prohibited by law: any public performance or display, including transmission of any image over a network; preparation of any derivative work, including the extraction, in whole or in part, of any images; any rental, lease, or lending of the program.

Chapter Overview

❖ Social Groups   ❖ Working for the Corporation

❖ Bureaucracies   ❖ Group Dynamics

Copyright © Allyn & Bacon 2006   2

Social Groups

❖ Aggregate - People Who Share a Space But Don't See Selves as Belonging

❖ A Category - People Who Share Characteristics

❖ A Group - People Who Think of Themselves as Belonging Together

Copyright © Allyn & Bacon 2006   3

Teachers are groups
students are groups

Social Groups

❖Primary Groups

  ❖Face-to-Face

  ❖The Family

  ❖Friends

❖Producing a Mirror Within

Copyright © Allyn & Bacon 2006   4

Social Groups

❖Secondary Groups

  ❖Larger, More Anonymous

  ❖Members Interact Based on Roles

  ❖Fail to Satisfy Need for Intimate Association

Copyright © Allyn & Bacon 2006   5

Voluntary Associations

❖Organized on Basis of Mutual Interest

❖The Inner Circle and Iron Law of

  Oligarchy

Copyright © Allyn & Bacon 2006   6

In-Groups and Out-Groups

❖In-Groups and Out-Groups Produce…

❖Loyalty

❖Sense of Superiority

❖Rivalries

❖Implications for Socially Diverse Society

7

Reference Groups

❖Groups Used as Standards to Evaluate

Selves

❖Provide a Yardstick

❖Exposes Us to Contradictory Standards

8

Social Networks

❖Ties that Extend Outward from Self

❖The Small World Phenomenon

❖Is the Small World Phenomenon a Myth?

9

Social Networks

❖Implications for Socially Diverse Society

❖Implications for Science

Copyright © Allyn & Bacon 2006   10

Electronic Communities

❖People Connect Online

❖Newsgroups

❖Online Chat Rooms

Copyright © Allyn & Bacon 2006   11

Bureaucracies

❖ Five Characteristics of Bureaucracies

❖ Clear Cut Levels

❖ Division of Labor

❖ Written Rules

❖ Written Communication and Records

❖ Impersonality

Copyright © Allyn & Bacon 2006   12

1) The boss

Perpetuation of Bureaucracies

❖ Take on a Life of Own

❖ Suffers from Goal Displacement

❖ March of Dimes Example

13

Coping with Bureaucracies

❖ Red Tape

❖ Bureaucratic Alienation

❖ Resisting Alienation

14

Working for the Corporation

❖ Stereotypes

❖ The "Hidden" Corporate Culture

  ❖ Hidden Values

  ❖ Self-Fulfilling Prophesies

❖ Iron Law of Oligarchy

15

Managing Diversity in the Workplace

❖ Half of Workers are Minorities, Immigrants, and Women

❖ Diversity Includes:

  ❖ Ethnicity
  ❖ Gender
  ❖ Age
  ❖ Religion
  ❖ Social Class
  ❖ Sexual Orientation

Copyright © Allyn & Bacon 2006

U.S. and Japanese Corporations

❖ Hiring and Promoting Teams

❖ Lifetime Security

❖ Almost Total Involvement

❖ Broad Training

❖ Decision Making by Consensus

Copyright © Allyn & Bacon 2006   17

U.S. and Japanese Corporations

❖ Myth vs. Reality

  ❖ Differences Less than in the Past

  ❖ Global Competition Causes Interdependencies

  ❖ Technology Affecting Worker Behavior

Copyright © Allyn & Bacon 2006   18

Group Dynamics

❖ Group Size Affects Stability and Intimacy
  ❖ Dyad
  ❖ Triad
  ❖ Coalitions

Group Dynamics

❖ Group Size Affects Stability and Intimacy
  ❖ Dyad
❖ Triad
  ❖ Coalitions
❖ As Size Increases, So Does Stability
❖ As Size Increases, Intensity and Intimacy Decreases

20

Group Dynamics

❖ Effects of Group Size on Attitudes and Behavior
❖ The Larger the Group…
  ❖ Greater Diffusion of Responsibility
  ❖ Increase in Formality
  ❖ Division into Smaller Groups

21

Leadership

❖ Leaders are People Who Influence Others'

Behaviors, Opinions, and Attitudes

❖ Who Becomes a Leader?

❖ Instrumental and Expressive Leaders

Copyright © Allyn & Bacon 2006   22

Leadership

❖Leadership Styles

  ❖Authoritarian

  ❖Democratic

  ❖Laissez-Faire

❖Leadership Styles in Changing Situations

Copyright © Allyn & Bacon 2006   23

Power of Peer Pressure and Authority

❖The Asch Experiment

❖The Milgram Experiment

Copyright © Allyn & Bacon 2006   24

The Asch's Choose an answer based on surrounding

Groupthink

❖Collective Tunnel Vision Groups Develop

❖Global Consequences of Group

Dynamics

❖Preventing Groupthink

25

_____

_____

_____

_____

_____

_____

_____

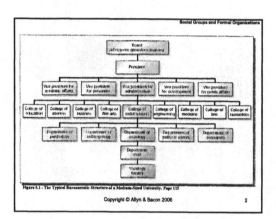

Figure 5.1 - The Typical Bureaucratic Structure of a Medium-Sized University. Page 115

Copyright © Allyn & Bacon 2006

2

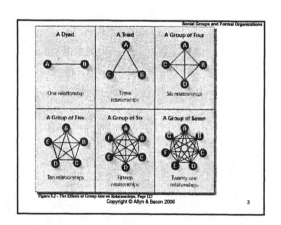

Figure 5.2 - The Effects of Group Size on Relationships. Page 123

Copyright © Allyn & Bacon 2006

3

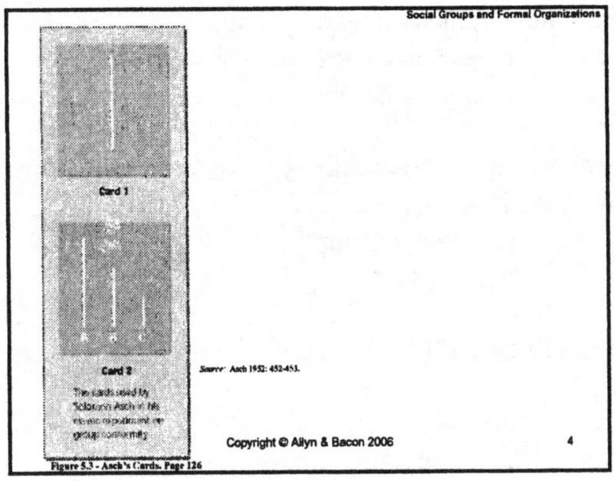

Card 1

Card 2

Source: Asch 1952: 452-453.

The cards used by Solomon Asch in his experiments on group conformity.

Figure 5.3 - Asch's Cards. Page 126

4

_____

_____

_____

_____

_____

_____

_____

PRACTICE TEST

1. The male students in the class all have brown eyes. These students make up a/an:
   a. category
   b. primary group
   c. secondary group
   d. aggregate

2. Today at the grocery store, while waiting to be checked out by the cashier, you waited in line with eight other people. This collection of people would constitute a:
   a. category
   b. aggregate
   c. social group
   d. network

3. All the sports fans around the world who consider the Pittsburgh Steelers their favorite NFL team comprise a/an:
   a. category
   b. in-group
   c. out-group
   d. aggregate

4. Leo Anthony is a music theory major at a prestigious art school. His classes are small and composed of other music majors who spend a great deal of time together outside the classroom socializing as well as helping each other prepare for exams and projects. Of the following choices, Leo and his classmates would best be considered a/an:
   a. aggregate
   b. primary group
   c. secondary group
   d. category

5. Of the following characteristics, which one *is least* applicable to secondary groups?
   a. personal and face-to-face
   b. large and anonymous
   c. common interest or activity
   d. formal

6. The term "iron law of oligarchy" was coined by:
   a. Robert Michels
   b. Rosabeth Kanter
   c. Irving Janis
   d. Clark Griswald

7. What are out-groups?
   a. groups who practice the values of mainstream society in an outstanding manner
   b. groups supporting rebellion against mainstream values
   c. groups towards which a particular person or group feels antagonism
   d. groups towards which a particular person or group feels loyalty

8. The groups we use as standards to evaluate ourselves are called
   a. primary groups.
   b. reference groups.
   c. voluntary groups.
   d. looking-glass groups.

9. Ties that extend outward from an individual, gradually encompassing more and more people including professional contacts, friends, friends of friends, and mere acquaintances comprise:
   a. the small world phenomenon
   b. an electronic community
   c. the hidden universe
   d. a social network

10. The small world phenomenon was an experiment conducted by Stanley Milgram that featured participants who acted as:
    a. prisoners and guards
    b. students and teachers
    c. senders and receivers
    d. supervisors and employees

11. Which of the following *is not* a characteristic of the bureaucracy?
    a. Assignments flow down the chain of command and accountability flows upward.
    b. A division of labor where each worker has a specific task to fulfill.
    c. Written rules and well kept records.
    d. Personal attention and a feeling of being irreplaceable to the organization.

12. The first theorist to identify the essential characteristics of an "ideal" bureaucracy was
    a. August Comte.   c. Max Weber.
    b. Karl Marx.   d. Emile Durkheim.

13. When the March of Dimes changed its mission from finding a vaccine to stop polio to fighting birth defects, it was practicing a technique common to bureaucracies called:
    a. bureaucratic ritualism   c. bureaucratic alienation
    b. corporate exchange   d. goal displacement

14. Marx termed the reaction of workers to being treated only according to roles and rules as:
    a. positivism   b. determinism   c. alienation   d. false consciousness

15. When workers begin to feel more like objects than people, Marx said they were experiencing:
    a. resistance   c. alienation
    b. bureaucracy   d. rationalization

16. The term coined by Max Weber that means bureaucracies would increasingly govern our lives through rules, regulations, and emphasis on results is:
    a. bureaucratic ritualism   c. the hidden corporate curriculum
    b. the rationalization of society   d. bureaucratic alienation

17. Which of the following *is not* one of the five ways Japanese corporations differ from United States corporations as pinpointed by William Ouchi?
    a. Specialization is encouraged in Japanese industry to stay on top of technology.
    b. Lifetime security within the Japanese company is taken for granted.
    c. In Japan, work is like a marriage with worker and company committed to one another.
    d. Decision making is done by consensus, each person affected by a decision is consulted.

18. The sociologist who addressed small group dynamics in his research in the early 1900's was:
    a. Herbert Spencer   c. Talcott Parsons
    b. Georg Simmel   d. Karl Marx

19. A newlywed couple is an example of a:
    a. triad   c. secondary group
    b. dyad   d. bureaucracy

20. The least stable type of group is a
    a. triad.   c. dyad.
    b. out-group.   d. primary group.

21. As a small group grows larger, it becomes more _____, but its _____ decreases.
    a. stable/intimacy   c. populated/membership
    b. intensity/stable   d. diversity/flexibility

22. Another name for the socioemotional leader is the:
    a. instrumental leader
    b. laissez-faire leader
    c. democratic leader
    d. expressive leader

23. George Patton was a brilliant and capable general in WWII known for his ability to take military objectives. He insisted on doing things his way and was often in trouble with his superiors. Some of his men highly respected him, others despised him. Based upon this description of General Patton which of the following leadership traits best fit him?
    a. expressive in type and authoritarian in style
    b. instrumental in type and democratic in style
    c. instrumental in type and authoritarian in style
    d. expressive in type and laissez faire in style

24. The classic experiment on group conformity involving a comparison of lines was conducted by:
    a. Solomon Asch
    b. Stanley Milgram
    c. Rosabeth Kanter
    d. Georg Simmel

25. The term that refers to collective tunnel vision coined by Irving Janis is:
    a. groupthink
    b. bureaucratic ritualism
    c. group polarization
    d. bureaucratic solidarity

PRACTICE TEST — ANSWER KEY

1. A (page 109)
2. B (page 109)
3. A (page 109)
4. B (page 109)
5. A (page 110)
6. A (page 111)
7. C (page 111)
8. B (page 112)
9. D (page 113)

10. A (pages 113-114)
11. D (pages 115-116)
12. C (page115)
13. D (page 116)
14. C (page 117)
15. C (page 117)
16. B (page 117)
17. A (page 120)
18. B (page 121)

19. B (page 121)
20. C (page 121)
21. A (page 121-123)
22. D (page 124)
23. C (pages 124-125)
24. A (pages 125-126)
25. A (page 127)

CHAPTER 6

DEVIANCE AND SOCIAL CONTROL

KEY TERMS

capitalist class: the wealthy who own the means of production and buy the labor of the working class

control theory: the idea that two control systems—inner controls and outer controls—work against our tendencies to deviate

crime: the violation of norms that are written into law

criminal justice system: the system of police, courts, and prisons set up to deal with people who are accused of having committed a crime

cultural goals: the legitimate objectives held out to the members of a society

deviance: the violation of rules or norms

differential association: Edwin Sutherland's terms to indicate that associating with some groups results in learning an "excess of definitions" of deviance (attitudes favorable to committing deviant acts), and, by extension, in a greater likelihood that their members will become deviant

genetic predispositions: inborn tendencies

hate crime: a crime with more severe penalties attached because it is motivated by hatred (dislike, animosity) of someone's race-ethnicity, religion, sexual orientation, or disability

illegitimate opportunity structures: opportunities for crimes woven into the texture of life

institutionalized means: approved ways of reaching cultural goals

labeling theory: the view, developed by symbolic interactionists, that the labels people are given affect their own and others' perceptions of them, thus channeling their behavior either into deviance or into conformity

marginal working class: the most desperate members of the working class, who has few skills, have little job security, and are often unemployed

medicalization of deviance: to make some deviance a medical matter, a symptom of some underlying illness that needs to be treated by physicians

negative sanction: an expression of disapproval for breaking a norm; ranging from a mild, informal reaction such as a frown to a formal prison sentence or even capital punishment

personality disorders: as a theory of deviance, the view that a personality disturbance of some sort causes an individual to violate social norms

positive sanction: reward or positive reaction for following norms, ranging from a smile to a prize

recidivism rate: the proportion of persons who are rearrested

social control: a group's formal and informal means of enforcing norms

social order: a group's customary social arrangements

stigma: "blemishes" that discredit a person's claim to a "normal" identity

strain theory: Robert Merton's term for the strain engendered when a society socializes large numbers of people to desire a cultural goal (such as success) but withholds from many the approved means to reach that goal; one adaptation to the strain is deviance, including crime, the choice of an innovative means (one outside the approved system) to attain the cultural goal

street crime: crimes such as mugging, rape, and burglary

techniques of neutralization: ways of thinking or rationalizing that help people deflect society's norms

white-collar crime: Edwin Sutherland's term for crimes committed by people of respectable and high social status in the course of their occupations

working class: those who sell their labor to the capitalist class

KEY PEOPLE

Walter Becker: Becker observed that an act is not deviant in and of itself, but only when there is a reaction to it.

William Chambliss: Chambliss demonstrated the power of the label in his study of two youth gangs—the Saints and the Roughnecks.

Richard Cloward and Lloyd Ohlin: These sociologists identified the illegitimate opportunity structures that a woven into the texture of life in urban slums and provide an alternative set of opportunities for slum residents when legitimate ones are blocked.

Emile Durkheim: Durkheim noted the functions that deviance has for social life.

Robert Edgerton: This anthropologist's studies document how different human groups react to similar behaviors, demonstrating that what is deviant in one context is not in another.

Erving Goffman: Goffman wrote about the role of stigma in the definition of who and what is deviant.

Travis Hirschi: Hirschi studied the strength of the bonds an individual has to society in order to understand the effectiveness of inner controls.

Ruth Horowitz: Horowitz did participate observation in a lower-class Chicano neighborhood in Chicago and discovered how associating with people who have a certain concept of "honor" can propel young men to deviance.

Martin Sanchez Jankowski: Jankowski studied gangs and identified traits that characterize gang members and identifying the function that gangs play in urban neighborhoods.

Robert Merton: Merton developed strain theory to explain patterns of deviance within a society.

Walter Reckless: Reckless developed control theory, suggesting that our behavior is controlled by two different systems, one external (*outer controls* like the police, family, and friends) and the other internal (*inner controls* like our conscience, religious principles, and ideas of right and wrong).

Edwin Sutherland: Sutherland not only developed differential association theory, but was the first to study and give a name to crimes that occur among the middle class in the course of their work—white collar crime.

Gresham Sykes and David Matza: These sociologists studied the different strategies delinquent boys use to deflect society's norms—techniques of neutralization.

Thomas Szasz: Szasz argued that mental illness represents the medicalization of deviance.

Mark Watson: Watson studied motorcycle gangs and found that these people actively embraced the deviant label.

Essentials of Sociology

Sixth Edition

Chapter Six: Deviance and Social Control

Chapter Overview

- ❖ What is Deviance?
- ❖ The Symbolic Interactionist Perspective
- ❖ The Functionalist Perspective
- ❖ The Conflict Perspective
- ❖ Reactions to Deviance

What is Deviance?

"It is not the act itself, but the reaction to the act, that make something deviant."

Howard Becker, 1966

3

What is Deviance?

❖ Relative Deviance

❖ What is Deviant to Some is not

   Deviant to Others

❖ "Deviance" is Nonjudgmental

   Term

Copyright © Allyn & Bacon 2006   4

_____
_____
_____
_____
_____
_____

Deviance Terminology

❖ Deviance
   ❖Violation of Rules or Norms
❖ Crime
   ❖Violation of Norms as Laws
❖ Stigma
   ❖Blemishes on "Normal" Identity

Copyright © Allyn & Bacon 2006   5

_____
_____
_____
_____
_____
_____

Norms and Social Life

❖ Norms Make Social Life Possible by

   Making Behavior Predictable

❖ Norms Bring Social Order

❖ Social Control - Formal and Informal

   Means of Enforcing Norms

Copyright © Allyn & Bacon 2006   6

_____
_____
_____
_____
_____
_____
_____

Sanctions

❖Negative Sanctions

❖Positive Sanctions

Copyright © Allyn & Bacon 2006   7

Explanations of Deviance
❖Sociobiology
  ❖Look for Answers Inside Individuals
  ❖Genetic Predispositions
❖Psychologists
  ❖Focus on Conditions Within Individuals
  ❖Personality Disorders
❖Sociology
  ❖Look for Answers Outside Individuals
  ❖Social Class

Copyright © Allyn & Bacon 2006   8

Symbolic Interactionist Perspective
Differential Association Theory

❖ Learn to Deviate or Conform

  Through Group Association

  ❖Families

  ❖Friends, Neighbors

  ❖Subculture

  ❖Prison or Freedom?

Copyright © Allyn & Bacon 2006   9

Symbolic Interactionist Perspective

Control Theory - Inner Controls

❖Morality

❖Conscience

❖Religious Principles

10

_____

_____

_____

_____

_____

_____

_____

Symbolic Interactionist Perspective

Control Theory - Outer Controls

❖Attachments

❖Commitments

❖Involvements

❖Beliefs that Actions are Morally Wrong

11

_____

_____

_____

_____

_____

_____

_____

Symbolic Interactionist Perspective

Labeling Theory

❖Focuses on the Significance of Labels

❖Labels Become Part of Self-Concept

❖Propel Towards or Away from Deviance

12

_____

_____

_____

_____

_____

_____

_____

Symbolic Interactionist Perspective
Rejecting Labels

❖Denial of Responsibility

❖Denial of Injury

❖Denial of a Victim

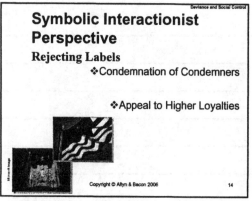

Copyright © Allyn & Bacon 2006   13

Symbolic Interactionist Perspective
Rejecting Labels
❖Condemnation of Condemners

❖Appeal to Higher Loyalties

Copyright © Allyn & Bacon 2006   14

Symbolic Interactionist Perspective
Labeling Theory

❖Embracing Labels - Outlaw Bikers

❖The Power of Labels - Saints and

Roughnecks

Copyright © Allyn & Bacon 2006   15

Functionalist Perspective

Can Deviance Be Functional?

❖ Clarifies Moral Boundaries and

   Affirms Norms

❖ Promotes Social Unity

❖ Promotes Social Change

16

Functionalist Perspective

Strain Theory

❖ Social Values Generate Crime

❖ Cultural Goals

❖ Institutional Means

❖ Strain Leads to Anomie

17

Functionalist Perspective

Four Deviant Paths

❖ Innovators

❖ Ritualism

❖ Retreatism

❖ Rebellion

18

Functionalist Perspective

Illegitimate Opportunity Structures

❖ Unequal Access to Institutional

   Means to Success

  ❖ Street Crime

  ❖ White-Collar Crime

  ❖ Gender and Crime

Copyright © Allyn & Bacon 2006   19

Conflict Perspective

Class, Crime, and the Judicial System

❖ Power and Inequality

  ❖ Capitalist Class

  ❖ Working Class

  ❖ Marginal Working Class

❖ The Law as an Instrument of

   Oppression

Copyright © Allyn & Bacon 2006   20

Reaction to Deviance

❖ Street Crime and Prisons

❖ The Decline of Crime

❖ Recidivism

❖ The Death Penalty Bias

Copyright © Allyn & Bacon 2006   21

Reaction to Deviance

❖ Legal Change

❖ Medicalization of Deviance

    ❖ Neither Mental nor Illness?

    ❖ Homeless Mentally Ill

❖ Need for More Humane Approach

22

Essentials of Sociology

Sixth Edition

Chapter Six: Deviance and Social Control

This multimedia product and its contents are protected under copyright law. The following are prohibited by law: any public performance or display, including transmission of any image over a network; preparation of any derivative work, including the extraction, in whole or in part, of any images; any rental, lease, or lending of the program.

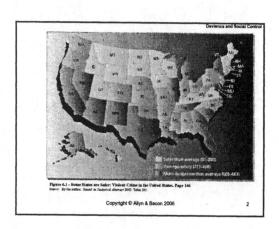

Figure 6.1 - Some States are Safer: Violent Crime in the United States. Page 146
Source: By the author. Based on *Statistical Abstract* 2002: Table 285.

Copyright © Allyn & Bacon 2006

2

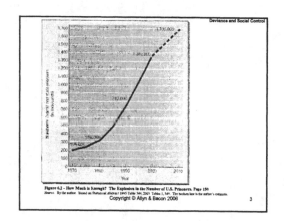

Figure 6.2 - How Much is Enough? The Explosion in the Number of U.S. Prisoners. Page 150
Source: By the author. Based on *Statistical Abstract* 1995: Table 349; 2003: Tables 1, 349. The broken line is the author's estimate.

Copyright © Allyn & Bacon 2006

3

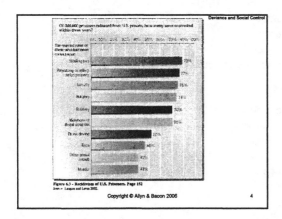

Figure 6.3 - Recidivism of U.S. Prisoners. Page 152
Source: Langan and Levin 2002.

Copyright © Allyn & Bacon 2006   4

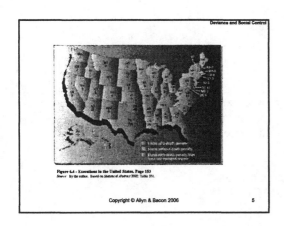

Figure 6.4 - Executions in the United States. Page 153
Source: By the author. Based on Statistical Abstract 2002: Table 351.

Copyright © Allyn & Bacon 2006   5

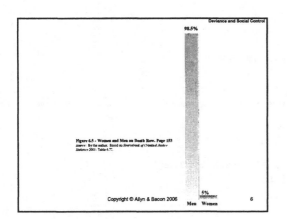

Figure 6.5 - Women and Men on Death Row. Page 153
Source: By the author. Based on Sourcebook of Criminal Justice Statistics 2001: Table 6.77.

Copyright © Allyn & Bacon 2006   6

PRACTICE TEST

1. Which of the following statements is *least true* of deviance?
   a. Deviance is an absolute within any respective culture.
   b. Deviance is any violation of norms.
   c. It is not the act itself, but the reaction to the act that makes something deviant.
   d. What is deviant to some is not deviant to others.

2. A violation of rules that have been written into law and enforced by the state is called a/an:
   a. morals violation
   b. crime
   c. rationalization
   d. sanction

3. Becker stresses the sociological perspective that deviance is
   a. established by the act itself, not the reaction of others.
   b. a violation of the formal, written laws of a society.
   c. defined by the same guidelines in every modern culture.
   d. defined by the reaction of others to the act.

4. Which statement is *least true* regarding norms?
   a. certain groups function quite well without having norms
   b. norms make social life predictable.
   c. without norms, there would be social chaos.
   d. norms are relative and not absolute.

5. Sentencing an armed robber to a lengthy prison sentence is an example of a:
   a. formal positive sanction
   b. informal positive sanction
   c. formal negative sanction
   d. informal negative sanction

6. The term "stigma" is usually associated with the sociologist:
   a. Howard Becker
   b. Erving Goffman
   c. Robert Merton
   d. Karl Marx

7. Social control refers to the:
   a. formal means for enforcing norms
   b. informal means for enforcing norms
   c. characteristics that discredit people
   d. both "a" and "b"

8. In looking for the explanation for deviance, psychologists focus upon:
   a. the structure of society
   b. personality disorders within the individual
   c. genetic predispositions
   d. theories of group behavior

9. Sociobiologists explain deviance:
   a. by assuming that people have genetic predispositions to becoming deviant
   b. by understanding the cultures within which people act
   c. through psychological tests
   d. through macrosociological perspectives only

10. The illustration for a clash of cultures used in the text that is referred to as "zij poj niam" involved a different interpretation of the proper way to:
    a. earn a living.
    b. raise children.
    c. negotiate a contract
    d. propose to and marry a woman.

11. The theory that explains deviant behavior as a learning process that takes place in close, intimate groups is:
    a. labeling theory.
    b. control theory.
    c. the theory of differential association
    d. containment theory

12. The concept of "techniques of neutralization" that are used by deviants to maintain a positive self image was developed by:
    a. Richard Cloward and Lloyd Ohlin
    b. Marvin Wolfgang and Franco Ferracuti
    c. Ben Peters and Thomas Heston
    d. Gresham Sykes and David Matza

13. All of the following are techniques of neutralization EXCEPT:
    a. denial of a victim
    b. denial the act occurred
    c. denial of responsibility
    d. denial of a right to appeal to higher loyalties

14. Jeremy has been shoplifting small items from the college bookstore, such as pens, pencils, and markers. He feels he is "borrowing" from the bookstore that will never miss these things or be negatively affected by the few dollars worth of merchandise he takes every week. Jeremy is employing the techniques of neutralization called:
    a. denial of responsibility
    b. denial of injury
    c. condemn the condemners
    d. appeal to higher loyalty

15. According to Chambliss, the most important characteristic distinguishing the Saints from the Roughnecks was their:
    a. rates of truancy.
    b. social class.
    c. rate of vandalism
    d. race and ethnicity

16. According to _____ deviance may actually provide a functional benefit for society.
    a. Emile Durkheim
    b. Karl Marx
    c. Max Weber
    d. Robert Merton

17. Functionalists like Emile Durkheim believe deviance
    a. hinders social unity.
    b. promotes social change.
    c. confuses what a society's moral boundaries entail.
    d. negates societal norms.

18. A sense of normlessness that is the basis of strain theory is called:
    a. anomie.
    b. social control.
    c. differential association.
    d. class conflict.

19. Which sociologist developed strain theory?
    a. Emile Durkheim
    c. Lloyd Ohlin
    b. Richard Cloward
    d. Robert Merton

20. According to strain theory, people who accept the goals of society but who use illegitimate means to try to achieve them would be classified as:
    a. a conformist
    c. a retreatist
    b. an innovator
    d. a rebel

21. The _____ perspective contends that the criminal justice system focuses its energies on the working class.
    a. functionalist
    c. conflict
    b. symbolic interactionist
    d. labeling

22. Which statement is *least true* of the conflict perspective as it pertains to deviance?
    a. Law is viewed as an instrument of oppression.
    b. The rich and powerful are able to bypass the court system.
    c. Laws reflect the consensus of society.
    d. The power elite controls the criminal justice system.

23. Conflict theorists believe that in the U.S. criminal justice system
    a. there is a significant focus on crimes by owners of corporations.
    b. the law does not operate impartially.
    c. the capitalist class is totally ignored in terms of being prosecuted for crime.
    d. courts imprison more white-collar crime offenders than street crime offenders.

24. Of the following crimes, which one has experienced the lowest increase among women?
    a. prostitution
    c. drug use
    b. illegal gambling
    d. burglary

25. The recidivism rate, which is the percentage of former prisoners who are rearrested is:
    a. extremely high
    c. unable to be calculated
    b. very low
    d. uncertain

PRACTICE TEST — ANSWER KEY

1. A (page 134)
2. B (page 134)
3. D (page 134)
4. A (pages 135-136)
5. C (page 136)
6. B (page 135)
7. D (page 136)
8. B (page 137)
9. A (page 137)

10. D (page 136-137)
11. C (page 138)
12. D (page 140)
13. B (page 140)
14. B (page 140-141)
15. B (page 141)
16. A (page 142)
17. B (page 142)
18. A (page 143)

19. D (page 143)
20. B (page 144)
21. C (pages 147-148)
22. C (pages 147-148)
23. B (pages 147-148)
24. B (page 147)
25. A (page 151)

CHAPTER 7

GLOBAL STRATIFICATION

KEY TERMS

bourgeoisie: Karl Marx's term for capitalists, those who own the means of production

caste system: a form of social stratification in which one's status is determined by birth and is lifelong

class consciousness: Karl Marx's term for awareness of a common identity based on one's position in the means of production

class system: a form of social stratification based primarily on the possession of money or material possessions

colonialism: the process by which one nation takes over another nation, usually for the purpose of exploiting its labor and natural resources

culture of poverty: the assumption that the values and behaviors of the poor perpetuate their poverty

dependency theory: the view that the Least Industrialized Nations have been unable to develop their economies because they grew dependent on the Most Industrialized Nations

divine right of kings: the idea that the king's authority comes directly from God

endogamy: the practice of marrying within one's own group

false consciousness: Karl Marx's term to refer to workers identifying with the interests of capitalists

globalization of capitalism: the adoption of capitalism around the globe

ideology: beliefs that justify social arrangements

means of production: the tools, factories, land, and investment capital used to produce wealth

meritocracy: a form of social stratification in which all positions are awarded on the basis of merit

multinational corporations: companies that operate across many national boundaries

neocolonialism: the economic and political dominance of the Least Industrialized Nations by the Most Industrialized Nations

proletariat: Karl Marx's term for workers (the exploited class that works for capitalists, those who own the means of production

slavery: a form of social stratification in which some people own other people

social class: a large number of people with similar amounts of income and education who work at jobs that are roughly comparable in prestige

social mobility: movement up or down the social class ladder

social stratification: the division of people into layers according to their relative power, property, and prestige; applies to both a society and to nations

world system: economic and political connections that tie the world's countries together

KEY PEOPLE

Randall Collins: Collins is a contemporary conflict theorist who has broadened conflict theory to include analysis of competition between groups within the same class for scarce resources.

Ralf Dahrendorf: Dahrendord is another contemporary conflict theorist who has argued that conflict over scarce resources is not just limited to class conflict.

Kingsley Davis and Wilbert Moore: These functionalists developed the theory of stratification that suggests inequality is universal because it helps societies survive by motivating the most qualified members of society to strive to fill the most important social positions.

William Domhoff: Domhoff has studied the social networks of the elite and documented how members of this group move in a circle of power that multiplies their opportunities.

John Kenneth Galbraith: This economist argued that the Least Industrialized Nations remain poor because their own culture holds them back.

Michael Harrington: Harrington saw that colonialism has been replaced by neocolonialism.

Martha Huggins: Huggins has studied poverty in the Least Industrialized Nations.

Gehard Lenski: Lenski offered a synthesis of functionalist and conflict view of stratification.

Gerda Lerner: This historian has noted that the first people who were enslaved as a result of war and conquest were women.

Oscar Lewis: Lewis is the anthropologist who first suggested the reason some people are poor is because they live in a culture of poverty.

Karl Marx: Marx concluded that social class depended exclusively on the means of production; an individual's social class depended on whether or not he owned the means of production.

Wright Mills: Mills is one of the 20th century conflict theorists who has broadened Marx's original theory to recognize other bases for conflict besides social class.

Gaetano Mosca: Mosca argued that every society is inevitably stratified by power.

James Schellenberg: Schellenberg is a contemporary conflict theorist.

Melvin Tumin: Tumin was the first to offer a criticism of the functionalist view on stratification.

Immanuel Wallerstein: Wallerstein proposed a world system theory to explain global stratification.

Max Weber: Weber argued social class was based on three components — class, status, and power.

Essentials of Sociology

Sixth Edition

Chapter Seven: Global Stratification

This multimedia product and its contents are protected under copyright law. The following are prohibited by law: any public performance or display, including transmission of any image over a network; preparation of any derivative work, including the extraction, in whole or in part, of any images; any rental, lease, or lending of the program.

Chapter Overview

- ❖ An Overview of Social Stratification
- ❖ What Determines Social Class?
- ❖ Why is Social Stratification Universal?
- ❖ How Do Elites Maintain Stratification?
- ❖ Comparative Social Stratification
- ❖ Global Stratification: Three Worlds
- ❖ How did the World's Nations Become Stratified?
- ❖ Maintaining Global Stratification

Copyright © Allyn & Bacon 2006

2

What is Social Stratification?

"A system in which groups of people are divided into layers according to their relative power, property and prestige."

Copyright © Allyn & Bacon 2006

3

Systems of Social Stratification

Slavery

- ❖ Causes
- ❖ Conditions
- ❖ Slavery in the New World
- ❖ Slavery Today

Copyright © Allyn & Bacon 2006   4

Systems of Social Stratification

Caste

- ❖ India's Religious Castes

- ❖ U.S. Racial Caste System

Copyright © Allyn & Bacon 2006   5

Systems of Social Stratification

Other

- ❖ Estate
- ❖ Class
- ❖ Global Stratification and Status of Females

Copyright © Allyn & Bacon 2006   6

Determinants of Social Class

Karl Marx: The Means of Production

❖Bourgeoisie

❖Proletariat

❖Class Consciousness

7

Determinants of Social Class

Max Weber

❖Property - Wealth

❖Prestige - Often Derived from Property

❖Power - Ability to Control Others

8

Why is Social Stratification Universal?

**Functionalists Perspective:
Motivating Qualified People**

❖Davis and Moore's Explanation

❖Society Must Make Sure all Positions are

Filled

9

Why is Social Stratification Universal?

**Functionalists Perspective:
Motivating Qualified People**

❖Davis and Moore's Explanation

    ❖Some Positions are More Important than

    Others

    10

_____

_____

_____

_____

_____

_____

Why is Social Stratification Universal?

**Functionalists Perspective:
Motivating Qualified People**

❖Davis and Moore's Explanation

    ❖More Important Positions Filled by More

    Qualified People

    11

_____

_____

_____

_____

_____

_____

Why is Social Stratification Universal?

**Functionalists Perspective:
Motivating Qualified People**

❖Davis and Moore's Explanation

    ❖To Motivate Qualified People, They Must

    Be Rewarded

    12

_____

_____

_____

_____

_____

_____

Why is Social Stratification Universal?

Tumin's Critique of Davis and Moore

❖ How do we know the positions most rewarded are most important?

❖ Society should be a meritocracy, it's not.

❖ If stratification is functional, it should benefit everyone.

Copyright © Allyn & Bacon 2006   13

Why is Social Stratification Universal?

The Conflict Perspective

❖ Mosca's Argument

   ❖ No Society Can Exist Unless Organized

   ❖ Leadership Means Inequalities of Power

   ❖ Human Nature is Self-Centered

Copyright © Allyn & Bacon 2006   14

Why is Social Stratification Universal?

The Conflict Perspective

❖ Marx's Argument

   ❖ Functionalist Explanation is Ideology of the Elite

   ❖ Class Consciousness Will Overcome Blinding Ideology

Copyright © Allyn & Bacon 2006   15

Why is Social Stratification Universal?

The Conflict Perspective

❖ Current Applications of Conflict Theory

   ❖ Struggle Between Labor and Capitalists

   ❖ Competition of Groups Within Class

   ❖ Relations Between Women and Men

❖ Lenski's Synthesis

16

How Do Elites Maintain Stratification?

❖ Ideology vs. Force

   ❖ Controlling Ideas

   ❖ Controlling Information and

      Using Technology

17

Comparative Social Stratification

❖ Social Stratification in

   Great Britain

❖ Social Stratification in

   Former Soviet Union

18

Global Stratification: Three Worlds

❖ First World - Industrialized Capitalist Nations

❖ Second World - Communist Nations

❖ Third World - Nations that Don't Fit in First Two

19

Global Stratification: Three Worlds

❖ Most Industrialized Nations

❖ Industrializing Nations

❖ Least Industrialized Nations

20

How Did World's Nations Become Stratified?

❖ Colonialism

❖ World System Theory

❖ Culture of Poverty

❖ Evaluating the Theories

21

Maintaining Global Stratification

❖ Neocolonialism

❖ Multinational Corporations

❖ Technology and Global Domination

22

_____

_____

_____

_____

_____

_____

_____

Essentials of Sociology
Sixth Edition

Chapter Seven: Global
Stratification

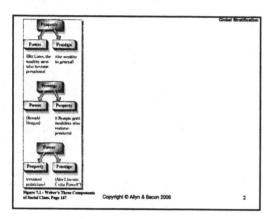

Figure 7.1 - Weber's Three Components of Social Class. Page 167   Copyright © Allyn & Bacon 2006   2

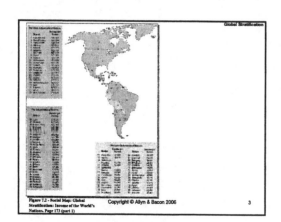

Figure 7.2 - Social Map: Global Stratification: Income of the World's Nations. Page 173 (part 1)   Copyright © Allyn & Bacon 2006   3

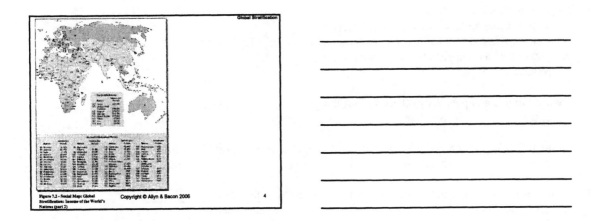

Figure 7.2 – Social Map: Global Stratification: Income of the World's Nations (part 2)

Copyright © Allyn & Bacon 2006

PRACTICE TEST

1. Social stratification refers to
   a. an individual's place in a social class hierarchy.
   b. a concept based on wealth, such as property, but not based on power.
   c. power only as it applies to wealth such as property.
   d. relative privileges.

2. Ownership of some people by others defines the _____ system.
   a. caste   b. estate   c. slavery   d. class

3. Of the following, which variable was not one on which slavery was initially based on?
   a. debt   b. crime   c. war   d. race

4. In the caste system, position in the stratification hierarchy is based on _____.
   a. achieved status   c. racial purity
   b. ascribed status   d. level of education

5. It is cultural tradition that members of the Jaconi tribe marry only other Jaconi who share a similar position on the stratification level. The Jaconi have established the practice of _____.
   a. endogamy   b. exogamy   c. heterogamy   d. monogamy

6. According to Marx, those who own the means of production are the _____.
   a. bourgeoisie   c. lumpenproletariat
   b. proletariat   d. petty bourgeoisie

7. According to Karl Marx, social class depends on a single factor, the _____.
   a. mode of production   c. race or ethnicity of the individual
   b. degree of consumption   d. amount of land they own

8. The mistaken notion held by workers that they themselves are capitalists and will someday share in the wealth of society is what Marx referred to as _____.
   a. class consciousness   c. group polarization
   b. social disorganization   d. false consciousness

9. Marx referred to the tools, factories, land, and investment capital used to produce wealth as:
   a. the means of production   c. class consciousness
   b. the mode of production   d. the lumpenproletariat

10. The outspoken critic of Karl Marx who said class was based on property, prestige, and power was _____.
    a. Max Weber   c. Kingsley Davis
    b. Gaetano Mosca   d. Wilbert Moore

11. The sociological perspective that stresses society's positions must be filled by the most qualified people is the:
    a. symbolic interactionist view   c. the conflict view
    b. functionalist view   d. neo-conflict view

106

12. Which of the following is NOT one of the components of social class as presented by Max Weber?
    a. Property
    b. Prestige
    c. Power
    d. Personality

13. Davis and Moore argued that stratification is inevitable because
    a. some positions are more important than others.
    b. the more important positions must be filled by the more qualified people.
    c. to motivate the more qualified people to fill these positions, society must offer them greater rewards.
    d. all of the above are true

14. Gerhard Lenski based his explanation on whether or not a society is held together by the principles of functionalism or conflict is based primarily on their:
    a. degree of ethnic purity
    b. degree of surplus
    c. economic system
    d. level of technological advancement

15. In Great Britain, the primary method in which class is perpetuated from one generation to the next is based on:
    a. race   b. income   c. education   d. political party

16. The method of stratification that involves the process of one nation taking over another by military force, popular in the 19th century, was called:
    a. dependency theory
    b. colonialism theory
    c. world systems theory
    d. multinationalism theory

17. World Systems Theory was developed by _____ to explain how global stratification came about..
    a. Karl Marx
    b. Max Weber
    c. Melvin Tumin
    d. Immanuel Wallerstein

18. The concept that some nations are crippled by a way of life that perpetuates poverty is an argument presented by economist _____.
    a. John Kenneth Galbraith
    b. Immanuel Wallerstein
    c. Melvin Tumin
    d. Gerhard Lenski

19. The classification *Most Industrialized Nations* includes
    a. Canada, Brazil, and the United States.
    b. the United States, Switzerland, and South Africa.
    c. France, Germany, and Australia.
    d. Japan, Kuwait, and the United States.

20. The classification of nations that has the highest percentage of the world's population and earth's land masses is the:
    a. Most Industrialized Nations
    b. The First World Nations
    c. Least Industrialized Nations
    d. Second World Nations

21. One significant characteristic of the Least Industrialized Nations is the fact that
    a. they occupy three-fourths of the land's surface.
    b. they represent over two-thirds of the world's population.
    c. most residents now have access to trained physicians.
    d. these countries have a low percentage of the overall growth rate of the world population.

22. Immanuel Wallerstein's theory on world system notes that
    a. periphery nations develop more than core nations.
    b. Germany was the first to become a core nation.
    c. most African countries are fringe nations.
    d. Britain, Holland, and France are core nations.

23. The difference between colonialism and neocolonialism is primarily that in neocolonialism:
    a. the military influence of the dominating country is less obvious.
    b. the dominating country improves the standard of living across the board in the developing country.
    c. classes within the developing nation shrink.
    d. democracy is established as well as capitalism.

24. Multinational corporations:
    a. are companies that operate across many national boundaries.
    b. help to maintain the global dominance of the Most Industrial Nations.
    c. are based predominantly in the Least Industrialized Nations.
    d. both a and b are correct.

25. The "Asian Tigers" refers to:
    a. a talented baseball team that has developed in Taiwan after it embraced capitalism.
    b. the dominant Chinese influence that has threatened capitalism in weaker nations.
    c. Pacific Rim nations with advanced capitalism that challenge older capitalist nations.
    d. Asian nations with vast economies based on the military industrial complex.

PRACTICE TEST — ANSWER KEY

1. D (page 160)
2. C (page 160)
3. D (page 160)
4. B (pages 160-161)
5. A (page 162)
6. A (page 165)
7. A (page 165)
8. D (page 166)
9. A (page 165)

10. A (page 166)
11. B (page 166)
12. D (page 166)
13. D (page 167)
14. D (page 169)
15. C (page 171)
16. B (page 176)
17. D (page 176)
18. A (page 177)

19. C (page 172)
20. C (pages 172-173)
21. B (page 173)
22. D (page 176)
23. A (page 180)
24. D (page 180)
25. C (page 181)

CHAPTER 8

SOCIAL CLASS IN THE UNITED STATES

KEY TERMS

contradictory class location: Erik Wright's term for a position in the class structure that generates contradictory interests

culture of poverty: the values and behavior of the poor that are assumed to make them fundamentally different from other people; these factors are assumed to be largely responsible for their poverty, and parents are assumed to perpetuate poverty across generations by passing these characteristics on to their children

downward social mobility: movement down the social class ladder

exchange mobility: about the same numbers of people moving up and down the social class ladder, such that in the end the social class system shows little change

feminization of poverty: a trend in U.S. poverty whereby most poor families are headed by women

Horatio Alger myth: a belief that anyone can get ahead if only he or she tries hard enough; encourages people to strive to get ahead and deflects blame for failure from society to the individual

intergenerational mobility: the change that family members make in social class from one generation to the next

poverty line: the official measure of poverty; calculated as three times a low-cost food budget

power: the ability to get your way, even over the resistance to others

power elite: C. Wright Mills's term for top leaders of corporations, military, and politics who make the nation's major decisions

prestige: respect or regard

social class: a large number of people with similar amounts of income and education who work at jobs that are roughly comparable in prestige

status: the position that someone occupies in society or a social group; one's social ranking

status consistency: people ranking high or low on all three dimensions of social class

status inconsistency: a contradiction or mismatch between statuses; a condition in which a person ranks high on some dimensions of social class or low on others

structural mobility: movement up or down the social class ladder that is due to changes in the structure of society, not to individual efforts

underclass: a small group of people for whom poverty persists year after year and across generations

upward social mobility: movement up the social class ladder

wealth: property and income

KEY PEOPLE

William Domhoff: Drawing upon the work of C. Wright Mills, Domhoff analyzed the workings of the ruling class

Dennis Gilbert and Joseph Kahl: These sociologists developed a more contemporary stratification model based on Max Weber's work.

Ray Gold: In research on status inconsistency, Gold studied tenant reactions to janitors who earned more than they did. He found that the tenants acted "snooty" to the janitors, and the janitors took pleasure in knowing the intimate details of the tenants lives.

Daniel Hellinger and Dennis Judd: In analyzing the exercise of power in the U.S., these two men suggest that there is a "democratic façade" that conceals the real sources of power within this society.

Elizabeth Higginbotham and Lynn Weber: These sociologists studied the mobility patterns for women. They found that those women who experienced upward mobility were most likely to have strong parental support to defer marriage and get an education.

Gerhard Lenski: Lenski noted that everyone wants to maximize their status, but that others often judge them on the basis of their lowest status despite the individual's efforts to be judged on the basis of his highest status.

Wright Mills: Mills used the term power elite to describe the top decision-makers in the nation.

Daniel J. Moynihan: Moynihan is a sociologist as well as U.S. senator; he attributes the high rate of child poverty to the breakdown of the U.S. family.

Max Weber: Weber expanded the concept of social class beyond economics—one's relationship to the means of production—to include power and prestige as well.

Erik Wright: Wright proposed an updated version of Marx's theory of stratification.

Essentials of Sociology
Sixth Edition

Chapter Eight: Social Class in the United States

This multimedia product and its contents are protected under copyright law. The following are prohibited by law: any public performance or display, including transmission of any image over a network; preparation of any derivative work, including the extraction, in whole or in part, of any images; any rental, lease, or lending of the program.

Chapter Overview

- ❖ What is Social Class?
- ❖ Social Mobility
- ❖ Sociological Models of Social Class
- ❖ Poverty
- ❖ Consequences of Social Class

2

What is Social Class?

Social Class

A large group of people who rank closely to one another in wealth, power, and prestige.

3

Components of Social Class

❖ Wealth - Value of a Person's Assets
  ❖ Property and Income
  ❖ Distinguishing Between Wealth & Income
  ❖ Distribution of Income

❖ Power
  ❖ Democratic Façade
  ❖ Power Elite

Copyright © Allyn & Bacon 2006

Components of Social Class

❖ Occupations and Prestige
  ❖ They Pay More
  ❖ They Require More Education
  ❖ They Entail More Abstract Thought
  ❖ They Offer Greater Autonomy

Copyright © Allyn & Bacon 2006

Components of Social Class

❖ Displaying Prestige

❖ Status Inconsistency

Copyright © Allyn & Bacon 2006   6

Sociological Models of Social Class

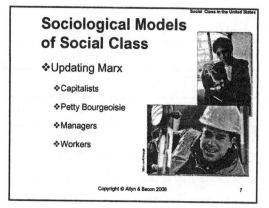

❖Updating Marx

  ❖Capitalists

  ❖Petty Bourgeoisie

  ❖Managers

  ❖Workers

7

Sociological Models of Social Class

❖Updating Weber

  ❖Capitalist Class

  ❖The Upper Middle Class

  ❖The Lower Middle Class

  ❖The Working Class

  ❖The Working Poor

  ❖The Underclass

❖Social Class in the Automobile Industry

8

Consequences of Social Class

❖Family Life

  ❖Choice of Husband or Wife

  ❖Divorce

❖Education

❖Religion

9

Consequences of Social Class

❖Politics

❖Physical Health

❖Mental Health

  ❖Mental Illness and Inequality in Health Care

Copyright © Allyn & Bacon 2006   10

Social Mobility

❖Three Types of Social Mobility

  ❖Upward

  ❖Downward

  ❖Exchange

Copyright © Allyn & Bacon 2006   11

Social Mobility

❖Women and Social Mobility

❖New Technology and Fears of the Future

Copyright © Allyn & Bacon 2006   12

Poverty

❖Who are Poor?

  ❖Geography

  ❖Race-Ethnicity

  ❖Education

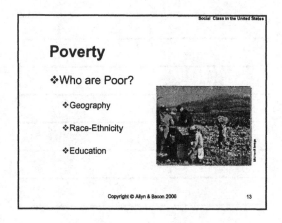

Copyright © Allyn & Bacon 2006   13

Poverty

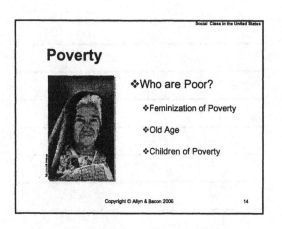

  ❖Who are Poor?

    ❖Feminization of Poverty

    ❖Old Age

    ❖Children of Poverty

Copyright © Allyn & Bacon 2006   14

Dynamics of Poverty

❖Culture of Poverty

❖Most Poverty is Short-lived

❖Number of Poor Relatively Stable

Copyright © Allyn & Bacon 2006   15

Poverty

❖Welfare Reform

  ❖Welfare Restructured in 1996

❖Conflict Theorists' Take on Welfare

16

Why are People Poor?

❖ Social Structure

❖ Features of Society

❖ Characteristics of

   Individuals

17

Poverty

❖Where is Horatio Alger?

❖Social Functions of a Myth

18

Essentials of Sociology

Sixth Edition

Chapter Eight: Social Class in the United States

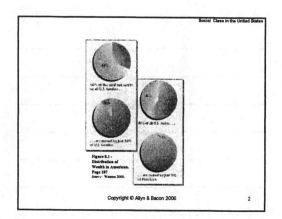

Figure 8.1 - Distribution of Wealth in America. Page 187
Source: Wolff 2000.

2

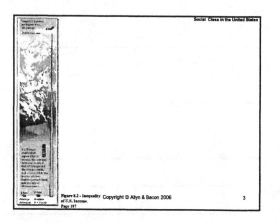

Figure 8.2 - Inequality of U.S. Income. Page 187

3

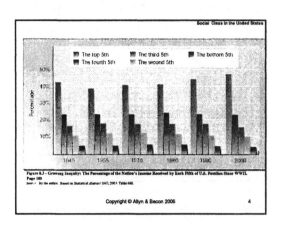

Figure 8.3 - Growing Inequity: The Percentage of the Nation's Income Received by Each Fifth of U.S. Families Since WWII. Page 188

Source: By the author. Based on Statistical Abstract 1947; 2003: Table 688.

4

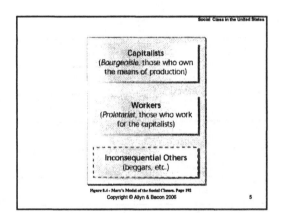

Capitalists
(*Bourgeoisie*, those who own the means of production)

Workers
(*Proletariat*, those who work for the capitalists)

Inconsequential Others
(beggars, etc.)

Figure 8.4 - Marx's Model of the Social Classes. Page 192

5

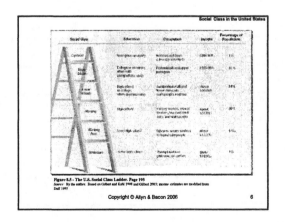

Figure 8.5 - The U.S. Social Class Ladder. Page 195

Source: By the author. Based on Gilbert and Kahl 1998 and Gilbert 2003; income estimates are modified from Duff 1995

6

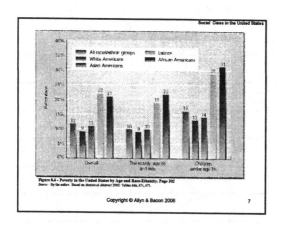

Figure 8.6 - Poverty in the United States by Age and Race-Ethnicity. Page 302
Source: By the author. Based on *Statistical Abstract* 2002: Tables 66b, 671, 673.

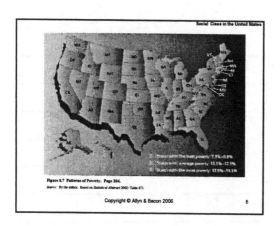

Figure 8.7 Patterns of Poverty. Page 304.
Source: By the author. Based on *Statistical Abstract* 2002: Table 673.

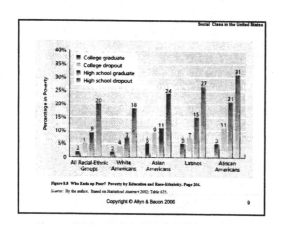

Figure 8.8 Who Ends up Poor? Poverty by Education and Race-Ethnicity. Page 304.
Source: By the author. Based on *Statistical Abstract* 2002: Table 675.

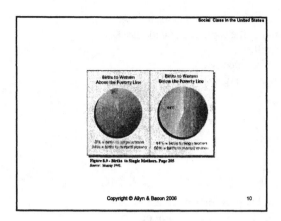

Figure 8.9 - Births to Single Mothers. Page 205
Source: Murray 1993.

Copyright © Allyn & Bacon 2006   10

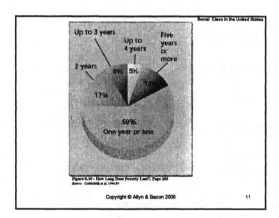

Figure 8.10 - How Long Does Poverty Last?. Page 206
Source: Gottschalk et al. 1994:89

Copyright © Allyn & Bacon 2006   11

PRACTICE TEST

1. Which statement regarding the distribution of wealth in the United States is *least true*?
   a. Wealth and income are relatively equally divided among the top three social classes.
   b. Americans as a whole are worth approximately $25 trillion.
   c. The top 20% of the population receives almost half of all income.
   d. The richest Americans have grown richer and the poor have grown poorer.

2. The top 10 % of the wealthiest families in America
   a. own 36% of all the wealth in America.
   b. own 40% of all the wealth in America.
   c. own 25% of all the wealth in America.
   d. own 68% of all the wealth in America.

3. The ability to carry out one's will despite resistance from others is referred to as:
   a. prestige   b. power   c. privilege   d. honor

4. The term coined by C. Wright Mills that refers to those who make the big decisions in U.S. society is:
   a. moral entrepreneurs   c. the power elite
   b. the Joint Chiefs   d. the national congress

5. Respect or regard bestowed upon someone as a result of a position they hold in life, such as their occupation, is referred to as:
   a. honor   b. power   c. master status   d. prestige

6. When a person has a similar ranking in all three dimensions of his or her social class, it is referred to as:
   a. Status Inconsistency   c. Master Status
   b. Status Consistency   d. Status Alignment

7. Joseph Kahl and Dennis Gilbert developed a model to portray social class in America based on _____ distinct classes.
   a. two   b. four   c. six   d. eight

8. The quality that shapes the upper middle class most from other classes is the:
   a. level of education among its members.
   b. number of minorities represented by it.
   c. pride members of this class have for doing "real work".
   d. middle class value system that it embraces.

9. The social class that has the highest percentage of membership is the:
   a. lower middle class   c. working class
   b. upper middle class   d. underclass

10. The characteristic that most applies to the working poor is that:
    a. they are the lowest class with little hope of climbing higher.
    b. they are concentrated in the inner city.
    c. most are high school dropouts and functionally illiterate.
    d. they include blue-collar and white-collar workers.

11. Which statement best describes the prevalence of divorce?
    a. Divorce is most common among the upper classes.
    b. Divorce is equally distributed among all classes.
    c. There is no relationship to the rate of divorce and social class.
    d. Divorce is most common among the lower classes.

12. In religion, Baptists draw heavily from the _____ classes while Methodists are more likely to be from the _____ class.
    a. lower/middle
    b. middle/upper
    c. middle/lower
    d. lower/upper

13. The higher one's social class, the more likely they will vote _____ while most members of the working class will vote _____.
    a. Democrat/Libertarian
    b. Republican/Democrat
    c. Democrat/Socialist Worker
    d. Republican/Independent

14. The lower a person's social class, the _____ that individual is to die before the expected age.
    a. less likely
    b. more likely
    c. lower the chance
    d. none of the above

15. Children who grow up in one social class, but end up in a different social class show
    a. intergenerational mobility.
    b. intragenerational mobility.
    c. horizontal mobility.
    d. downward social mobility.

16. The official measure of poverty that is based on the amount of income that a family must pay for food is called the:
    a. relative definition of poverty
    b. culture of poverty
    c. feminization of poverty
    d. poverty line

17. Which of the following is *not* a myth about poverty?
    a. Most of the poor are African Americans and Latinos.
    b. Most of the poor are single mothers and their children.
    c. Most of the poor live in suburban communities and rural areas.
    d. The poor live on welfare.

18. The total number of people living in poverty is highest for
    a. African-Americans and Latinos.
    b. males.
    c. Native Americans.
    d. whites.

19. Which region of the U.S. has had the highest rate of poverty for the last 100 years?
    a. the north
    b. the south
    c. the Midwest
    d. the west

20. Only _____ people who finish college end up in poverty.
    a. 2 out of 100
    b. 10 out of 100
    c. 23 out of 100
    d. 38 out of 100

21. Which of the following is *not* a reason for the feminization of poverty?
    a. Women have lower intellectual capability.
    b. Divorce.
    c. Births to single women.
    d. Lower wages paid to women.

22. The average length of time a family remains in poverty is:
    a. ten to twelve years.
    b. five to ten years.
    c. one to five years.
    d. less than one year.

23. From year to year the number of people in poverty:
    a. increases because of fewer government subsidies.
    b. deceases because of more government subsidies.
    c. remains about the same.
    d. cannot be accurately measured.

24. Sociologists prefer to explain poverty by:
    a. focusing on social structure.
    b. focusing on individual characteristics.
    c. by stressing the features of society that deny some people access to education or learning job skills.
    d. both a and c.

25. The rags-to-riches myth that anyone can overcome severe odds to become a startling success story is referred to as the _____ myth.
    a. Horatio Alger
    b. Johnnie Appleseed
    c. Prince and Pauper
    d. Abraham Lincoln

PRACTICE TEST — ANSWER KEY

1. A (page 187)
2. D (page 187)
3. B (page 187)
4. C (page 189)
5. D (page 190)
6. B (page 192)
7. C (page 195)
8. A (page 196)
9. C (page 196)

10. C (page 196)
11. D (page 198)
12. A (page 198)
13. B (page 198)
14. B (page 198)
15. A (page 200)
16. D (page 201)
17. C (page 202)
18. D (page 202-203)

19. B (page 203)
20. A (page 203)
21. A (pages 203-204)
22. B (page 206)
23. C (page 206)
24. D (page 206)
25. A (page 207)

INEQUALITIES OF RACE AND ETHNICITY

KEY TERMS

assimilation: the process of being absorbed into the mainstream culture

authoritarian personality: Theodor Adorno's term for people who are prejudiced and rank high on scales of conformity, intolerance, insecurity, respect for authority, and submissiveness to superiors

compartmentalize: to separate acts from feelings or attitudes

discrimination: an act of unfair treatment directed against an individual or a group

dominant group: the group with the most power, greatest privileges, and highest social status

ethnic cleansing: a policy of population elimination, including forcible expulsion and genocide

ethnicity (and ethnic): having distinctive cultural characteristics

ethnic work: activities designed to discover, enhance, or maintain ethnic/racial identification

genocide: the systematic annihilation or attempted annihilation of a race or ethnic group

individual discrimination: the negative treatment of one person by another on the basis of that person's perceived characteristics

institutional discrimination: negative treatment of a minority group that is built into a society's institutions

internal colonialism: the systematic economic exploitation of a minority group

melting pot: the idea that Americans of various backgrounds would melt (or merge), leaving behind their distinctive previous ethnic identities and forming a new ethnic group

minority group: people who are singled out for unequal treatment on the basis of their physical and cultural characteristics, and who regard themselves as objects of collective discrimination

multiculturalism (also called pluralism): a policy that permits or encourages groups to express their individual, unique racial and ethnic identities

pan-Indianism: the emphasis on the welfare of all Native Americans

pluralism: another term for multiculturalism

population transfer: involuntary movement of a minority group

prejudice: an attitude or prejudging, usually in a negative way

race: a group whose inherited physical characteristics distinguish it from other groups

racism: prejudice and discrimination on the basis of race

reserve labor force: the term used by conflict theorists for the unemployed, who can be put to work during times of high production and then discarded when no longer needed

rising expectations: the sense that better conditions are soon to follow, which, if unfulfilled, creates mounting frustration

scapegoat: an individual or group unfairly blamed for someone else's troubles

segregation: the policy of keeping racial or ethnic groups apart

selective perception: seeing certain features of an object or situation but remaining blind to others

split-labor market: a term used by conflict theorists for the practice of weakening the bargaining power of workers by splitting them along racial, ethnic, sex, age, and any other lines

WASP: a white Anglo-Saxon Protestant; narrowly, an American of English descent; broadly, an American of western European ancestry

white ethnics: white immigrants to the United States whose culture differs from that of WASPs

KEY PEOPLE

Theodor Adorno: Adorno identified the authoritarian personality type.

Lawrence Bobo and James Kluegel: In their research, these sociologists found that prejudice varied by age and educational level.

Emery Cowen, Judah Landes and Donald Schaet: In an experiment, t0hese psychologists found that students directed frustrations onto people who had nothing to do with their problem.

Ashley Doane: Doane identified four factors that affect an individual's sense of ethnic identity.

John Dollard: This psychologist first suggested that prejudice is the result of frustration and scapegoats become the targets for people's frustrations.

Raphael Ezekiel: This sociologist did participant observation of neo-Nazi and the Ku Klux Klan in order to examine racism from inside racist organizations.

Eugene Hartley: This psychologist is known for his work on prejudice. He found that people who are prejudiced against one racial or ethnic group tend to be prejudiced against others and that prejudice is not necessarily based on personal negative experiences.

Marie Krysan and Reynolds Farley: In a random sample of people in Detroit, these researchers found that both whites and African Americans judged Latinos as less intelligent than themselves.

Douglas Massey: Massey and his students designed a research project to test discrimination in the housing market. Students from different racial and social class backgrounds made calls about apartment units available for rent. When compared with white students, the African Americans were less likely to speak to a rental agent, less likely to be told a unit was available, more likely to have to pay an application fee, and more likely to have credit mentioned.

Ashley Montagu: this physical anthropologist pointed out that some scientists have classified humans into two races while others have identified as many as two thousand.

Donald Muir: Muir measured racial attitudes of white students who belonged to fraternities and sororities and compared them to nonmembers.

Alejandro Portes and Rueben Rumbaut: These sociologists looked at the impact that immigration has had on our country, noting that there has always been an anti-immigrant sentiment present.

Barbara Reskin: This sociologist examined the results of affirmative action, concluding that it has had only a modest impace on hiring, promotion, and college admission.

Muzafer & Caqrolyn Sherif: The Sherifs researched the functions of prejudice and found that it builds in-group solidaritiy.

Mark Wenneker and Arnold Epstein: These physicians studied patients admitted to Massachusetts hospitals for circulatory diseases or chest pain; they found that whites were 89 percent more likely to be given coronary bypass surgery.

Charles Willie: Willie has criticized William Wilson's work, arguing that race is still an important criterion for discrimination.

William Wilson: Wilson is known for his work on racial discrimination, in which he argues that class is a more important factor than race in explaining patterns of inequality.

Louis Wirth: Wirth offered a sociological definition of minority group.

Essentials of Sociology

Sixth Edition

Chapter Nine: Inequalities of
Race and Ethnicity

This multimedia product and its contents are protected under copyright law. The following are prohibited by law: any public performance or display, including transmission of any image over a network; preparation of any derivative work, including the extraction, in whole or in part, of any images; any rental, lease, or lending of the program.

Chapter Overview

❖ Laying the
Sociological
Foundation

❖ Race and Ethnic
Relations in the
United States

❖ Theories of
Prejudice

❖ Looking Toward
the Future

❖ Global Patterns of
Intergroup Relations

Copyright © Allyn & Bacon 2006   2

Race: Myth and Reality

❖ Race - Group with Distinguishing
Characteristics

❖ Myth 1 - Idea That Any Race is Superior
❖ All Races Have Geniuses and Idiots

❖ Myth 2 - Idea that Any Race is Pure
❖ Human Characteristics Flow Endlessly Together

Copyright © Allyn & Bacon 2006   3

Ethnic Groups

❖ Race Refers to Biological Characteristics

❖ Ethnicity Refers to Cultural Characteristics

❖ Common Ancestry

❖ Cultural Heritage

❖ Nations of Origin

Copyright © Allyn & Bacon 2006   4

Minority & Dominant Groups

❖ Minority Group - People Singled Out for Unequal Treatment

❖ Minority Group Can Be Racial or Ethnic

❖ Minority Group Not Necessarily Numerical Minority

Copyright © Allyn & Bacon 2006   5

Minority & Dominant Groups

❖ Dominant Group - Group with Most...

❖ Power

❖ Privileges

❖ Highest Social Status

❖ Dominant Groups Do the Discriminating

Copyright © Allyn & Bacon 2006   6

Emergence of Minority Groups

❖ Minority Group Occur Because of...

  ❖ Expansion of Political Boundaries

  ❖ Migration

❖ Minority Groups Share Characteristics

7

Shared Characteristics

❖ Membership is an Ascribed Status

❖ Physical or Cultural Traits Held in Low Esteem by Dominant Group

❖ Unequal Treatment

❖ Marry Within Own Group

❖ Feel Strong Group Solidarity

8

Constructing Racial-Ethnic Identity

❖ Relative Size

❖ Power

❖ Appearance

❖ Discrimination

❖ Ethnic Work

Learning Prejudice

❖ Discrimination is an Action

❖ Prejudice is an Attitude

❖ Learn from Association

   ❖KKK

   ❖Aryan Nation

❖ Far-Reaching Nature of Prejudice

Copyright © Allyn & Bacon 2006   10

Learning Prejudice

❖ Internalizing Dominant Norms

   ❖Media

   ❖Group Membership

❖ Prejudice Against Own Group

Copyright © Allyn & Bacon 2006   11

Ethnic Maps and Bias

❖ Home Mortgage and Car Loans

❖ Health Care

Copyright © Allyn & Bacon 2006   12

Theories of Prejudice

❖ Psychological Perspectives

  ❖ Frustration and Scapegoats

  ❖ The Authoritarian Personality

13

Theories of Prejudice

❖ Sociological Perspectives

  ❖ Functionalism

  ❖ Conflict Theory

  ❖ Symbolic Interactionism

    ❖ Labels Create Prejudice

    ❖ Self-Fulfilling Prophesy

14

Global Patterns of Intergroup Relations

❖ Genocide

❖ Population Transfer

❖ Internal Colonialism

15

Global Patterns of Intergroup Relations

❖ Segregation

❖ Assimilation

❖ Multiculturalism

Copyright © Allyn & Bacon 2006   16

Race and Ethnic Relations in the United States

European Americans

❖ Nation's Founders Included Only Those

from England (WASPs)

❖ Other "White" Europeans Inferior

Copyright © Allyn & Bacon 2006   17

Race and Ethnic Relations in the United States

Latinos

❖ Numbers Origins, Location

❖ Spanish Language

❖ Diversity

❖ Comparative Conditions

Copyright © Allyn & Bacon 2006   18

Race and Ethnic Relations in the United States

African Americans

❖ The Struggle for Civil Rights

❖ Rising Expectations and Civil Strife

❖ Continued Gains

19

___

Race and Ethnic Relations in the United States

African Americans

❖ Current Losses

❖ Race or Social Class? A Sociological Debate

❖ Racism as an Everyday Burden

20

___

Race and Ethnic Relations in the United States

Asian Americans

❖ Background of Discrimination

❖ Diversity

❖ Reasons for Success

   ❖ Family Life

   ❖ Educational Achievement

   ❖ Assimilation

21

Race and Ethnic Relations in the United States

Native Americans

❖ Diversity of Groups

❖ From Treaties to Genocide and Population Transfer

❖ The Invisible Minority and Self-Determination

22

_____

_____

_____

_____

_____

_____

_____

Looking Toward the Future

❖ The Immigration Debate

❖ Affirmative Action

❖ Towards a True Multicultural Society

23

_____

_____

_____

_____

_____

_____

_____

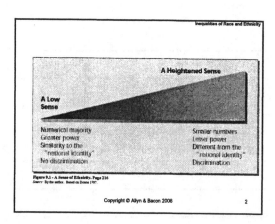

Figure 9.1 - A Sense of Ethnicity. Page 216
Source: By the author. Based on Doane 1997.

2

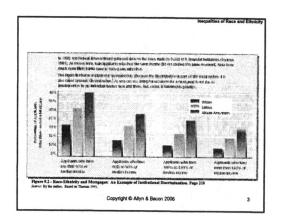

Figure 9.2 - Race-Ethnicity and Mortgages: An Example of Institutional Discrimination. Page 218
Source: By the author. Based on Thomas 1991.

3

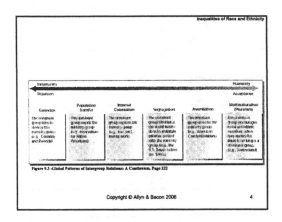

Figure 9.3 -Global Patterns of Intergroup Relations: A Continuum. Page 222

4

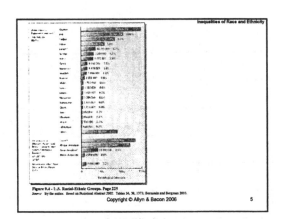

Figure 9.4 - U.S. Racial-Ethnic Groups. Page 225
Source: By the author. Based on Statistical Abstract 2002: Tables 36, 38, 1373; Bernstein and Bergman 2003.

5

Source: By the author. Based on Statistical Abstract 2002: Table 22.

Figure 9.5 - The Distribution of Dominant and Minority Groups. Page 226

6

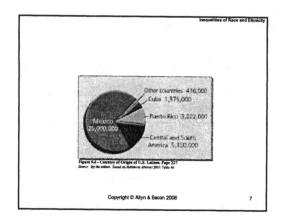

Figure 9.6 - Country of Origin of U.S. Latinos. Page 227
Source: By the author. Based on *Statistical Abstract* 2003: Table 46

7

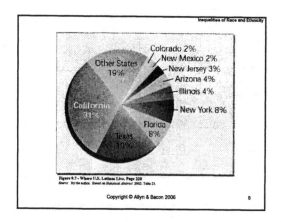

Figure 9.7 - Where U.S. Latinos Live. Page 228
Source: by the author. Based on *Statistical Abstract* 2002: Table 23.

8

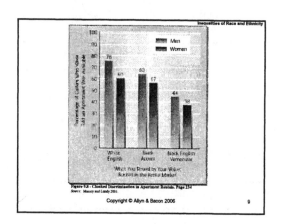

Figure 9.8 - Classical Discrimination in Apartment Rentals. Page 234
Source: Massey and Lundy 2001.

9

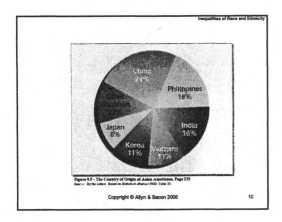

Figure 9.9 - The Country of Origin of Asian Americans. Page 235
Source: By the author. Based on *Statistical Abstract* 2002: Table 24.

10

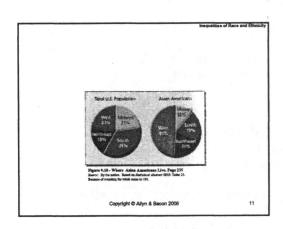

Figure 9.10 - Where Asian Americans Live. Page 235
Source: By the author. Based on *Statistical Abstract* 2003: Table 23.
Because of rounding the totals come to 101.

11

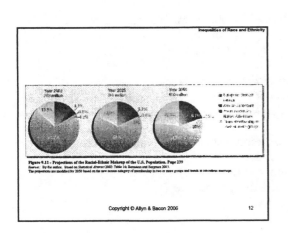

Figure 9.11 - Projections of the Racial-Ethnic Makeup of the U.S. Population. Page 239
Source: By the author. Based on *Statistical Abstract* 2002: Table 16; Bernstein and Bergman 2003.
The projections are modified for 2050 based on the new census category of membership in two or more groups and trends in interethnic marriage.

12

PRACTICE TEST

1. Ethnicity is based upon:
   a. biological characteristics and a feeling of peoplehood
   b. common ancestry and genetic disposition
   c. common ancestry and cultural heritage
   d. biological characteristics and genetic disposition

2. Sociological, the concept of minority group refers to:
   a. African-American, Latinos, and Asians.
   b. People who are singled out for unequal treatment and collective discrimination.
   c. The ethnic or racial group with the fewest members in society.
   d. Anyone who immigrates into a nation.

3. Sociologically, the people with the greatest power, most privileges, and highest social status are referred to as the:
   a. dominant group
   b. ruling class
   c. bourgeoisie
   d. capitalists

4. _____ is an action of unfair treatment directed against someone while _____ is an attitude that conveys negative prejudging.
   a. Domination/stereotyping
   b. Discrimination/profiling
   c. Discrimination/prejudice
   d. Domination/subjugation

5. What is individual discrimination?
   a. discrimination by one person against another
   b. discrimination against a group that is built into a society's social structure
   c. discrimination against all other groups by members of a particular social institution
   d. the perception by some that societal institutions are discriminatory

6. Unfair treatment directed against a group of people based on their ethnic or racial status that is woven into the fabric of society is referred to as:
   a. institutional discrimination
   b. individual discrimination
   c. dejure discrimination
   d. defacto discrimination

7. A racial, ethnic, or religious minority who is unfairly blamed for others' troubles are seen as:
   a. Racist
   b. Scapegoats
   c. Authorities
   d. Ethnocentric

8. The Authoritarian Personality Theory to explain prejudice was developed by:
   a. John Dollard
   b. Robert Merton
   c. Theodore Adorno
   d. Robert Muir

9. The sociological perspective that suggests prejudice and discrimination leads to group solidarity and can actually provide a positive incentive for society is the:
   a. symbolic interactionist perspective
   b. functionalist perspective
   c. conflict perspective
   d. neo-conflict perspective

10. When discussing the split labor market and reserve labor force as instruments of prejudice and discrimination, one is addressing the _____ perspective.
    a. conflict
    b. functionalist
    c. structural
    d. symbolic interactionist

11. In terms of prejudice, symbolic interactionists argue that:
    a. groups are pitted against one another and that benefits those in power.
    b. the labels we learn affect the way we see people.
    c. prejudice is functional.
    d. prejudiced people are insecure conformists.

12. The systematic annihilation of a race or ethnic group is referred to as:
    a. genocide
    b. subjugation
    c. population transfer
    d. assimilation

13. An impact of labeling that leads us to see certain things and be blind to others is referred to as:
    a. compartmentalization
    b. self-fulfilling prophecy
    c. selective perception
    d. group polarization

14. Another term for multiculturalism is:
    a. assimilation
    b. pluralism
    c. colonialism
    d. segregation

15. The best example of a society that has developed the approach of pluralism is that of
    a. America.
    b. Switzerland.
    c. Germany.
    d. South Africa.

16. The country that best exemplifies the intergroup relationship of pluralism is:
    a. Mexico   b. Brazil   c. Russia   d. Switzerland

17. The process of being absorbed into the mainstream culture is called
    a. pluralism.
    b. colonialism.
    c. assimilation.
    d. segregation.

18. The Naturalization Act of 1790 which was passed by the Continental Congress declared that:
    a. only men of any race, color, or creed could apply for American citizenship.
    b. all immigrants, regardless of sex, race, color, or creed could apply for citizenship.
    c. only white immigrants could apply for citizenship.
    d. all Europeans could apply for citizenship but not Asians or Africans.

19. In what year was the Civil Rights Act passed that made it illegal to discriminate in restaurants, theatres, and other public places?
    a. 1971   b. 1957   c. 1977   d. 1964

20. The 1896 Supreme Court case that addressed "separate but equal" accommodations for blacks was a reasonable use of state power was:
    a. the Dred Scott Decision
    b. Plessy vs. Ferguson
    c. Brown vs. Topeka Board of Education
    d. the Emancipation Proclamation

21. The 1955 incident in which Rosa Parks refused to give up her seat on a bus to a white person which inspired the Civil Rights Movement took place in:
    a. Savannah, Georgia
    b. Tupelo, Mississippi
    c. Montgomery, Alabama
    d. Richmond, Virginia

22. What separates most Latinos from other U.S. ethnic groups?
    a. The Spanish language
    b. Geographic distance
    c. State boundaries
    d. Residential patterns

23. The three largest groups of Asian Americans trace their heritage to:
    a. Vietnam, Cambodia, and the Philippines
    b. Vietnam, China, and Japan
    c. China, Indonesia, and Japan
    d. China, the Philippines, and Japan

24. The "Invisible Minority" refers to:
    a. African Americans
    b. Latino Americans
    c. Native Americans
    d. Asian Americans

25. The emphasis on common elements that run through Native American culture and develop an identity that goes beyond the tribe is called:
    a. Native Americanism
    b. Pan-Indianism
    c. American Indianism
    d. Nativism

PRACTICE TEST — ANSWER KEY

1. C (page 213)
2. B (Page 213)
3. A (page 215)
4. C (page 216)
5. A (page 218)
6. A (page 218)
7. B (page 219)
8. C (pages 219-220)
9. B (page 221)

10. A (page 221)
11. B (page 221)
12. A (page 221)
13. C (page 221)
14. B (page 222-223)
15. B (page 223)
16. D (page 223)
17. C (page 223)
18. C (page 225-226)

19. D (page 231)
20. B (page 229)
21. C (pages 229-230)
22. A (page 227)
23. D (page 235)
24. C (page 237)
25. B (page 238)

INEQUALITIES OF GENDER AND AGE

KEY TERMS

activity theory: the view that satisfaction during old age is related to a person's level and quality of activity

age cohort: people born at roughly the same time who pass through the life course together

ageism: prejudice, discrimination, and hostility directed against people because of their age, can be directed against any age group, including youth

dependency ratio: the number of workers required to support one person on Social Security

disengagement theory: the view that society prevents disruption by having the elderly vacate their positions of responsibility so that the younger generation can step into their shoes

feminism: the philosophy that men and women should be politically, economically, and socially equal; organized activity on behalf of this principle

gender: the social characteristics that a society considers proper for its males and females; masculinity and femininity

gender stratification: males' and females' unequal access to power, prestige, and property on the basis of sex

graying of America: older people making up an increasing proportion of the U.S. population

life expectancy: the age that someone can be expected to live to

life span: the maximum possible length of life

patriarchy: a society in which authority is vested in males; control by men of a society or group

quiet revolution: the fundamental changes in society that follow when vast numbers of women enter the work force

sex: biological characteristics that distinguish females and males, consisting of primary and secondary sex characteristics

sexual harassment: unwanted sexual advances, usually within an occupational or educational setting

KEY PEOPLE

Robert Butler: Butler coined the term "ageism" to refer to prejudice, discrimination and hostility directed against people because of their age.

Elaine Cumming and William Henry: These two developed disengagement theory to explain how society prevents disruption when the elderly vacate their positions of responsibility.

Janet Chafetz: Chafetz studied the second wave of feminism in the 1960s, noting that as large numbers of women began to work in the economy, they began to compare their working conditions with those of men.

Frederick Engels: Engels was a colleague of Karl Marx and wrote a book about the origins of the family in which he argued that male dominance developed with the origin of private property.

Sue Fisher: Fisher's participate observation in a hospital uncovered evidence of doctors' recommending unnecessary surgery for female patients.

Rex Fuller and Richard Schoenberger: These economists examined the starting salaries of business majors and found that women averaged 11 percent lower pay than men right out of college, and that the gap grew to 14 percent after five years in the workforce.

Marvin Harris: This anthropologist suggested that male dominance grew out of the greater strength that men had which made them better suited for the hand-to-hand combat of tribal societies; women became the reward to entice men into battle.

Charles Hart: An anthropologist who did his field work during the 1920s among the Tiwi.

Dorothy Jerrome: This anthropologist is critical of disengagement theory, pointing out that it contains implicit bias against old people.

Gerda Lerner: Lerner suggested that patriarchy may have had different origins in different places around the globe.

Meredith Minkler and Ann Robertson: These conflict sociologists investigated whether or not the government expenditures allocated for the elderly were at the expense of children and found there was no evidence of that.

Alice Rossi: This feminist sociologist has suggested that women are better prepared biologically for "mothering" than are men.

Felice Schwartz: Schwartz is the founder of Catalyst, an organization that focuses on women's issues in the workplace.

Diana Scully: Scully did research on physicians' attitudes towards female patients.

Christine Williams: Williams found that men in nontraditional careers and occupations often experience a glass escalator—moving more quickly than women into desirable work assignments, higher-level positions, and larger salaries.

Essentials of Sociology
Sixth Edition

Chapter Ten: Inequalities of
Gender and Age

This multimedia product and its contents are protected under copyright law. The following are prohibited by law: any public performance or display, including transmission of any image over a network; preparation of any derivative work, including the extraction, in whole or in part, of any images; any rental, lease, or lending of the program.

Chapter Overview

- ❖ Issues of Sex and Gender
- ❖ How Females Became a Minority Group
- ❖ Gender Inequality in the United States
- ❖ The Changing Face of Politics
- ❖ Aging in Global Perspective

- ❖ The Symbolic Interactionist Perspective
- ❖ The Functionalist Perspective
- ❖ The Conflict Perspective

Copyright © Allyn & Bacon 2006

2

What's Gender Stratification?

"Unequal Access to Power, Prestige, and Property on the Basis of Sex."

Copyright © Allyn & Bacon 2006

3

Issues of Sex and Gender

❖ Sex - Biological

Characteristics

  ❖Female and Male

  ❖Primary and Secondary Sexual

Characteristics

Copyright © Allyn & Bacon 2006   4

_____

_____

_____

_____

_____

_____

_____

Issues of Sex and Gender

❖ Gender - Social Characteristics

  ❖Masculinity and Femininity

  ❖Appropriate Behavior

Copyright © Allyn & Bacon 2006   5

_____

_____

_____

_____

_____

_____

_____

Gender Differences In Behavior Biology or Culture?

❖ Dominant Position in Sociology

  ❖Social Factors Primary, Not Biological

  ❖If Biological Should Be Less Variation in Male and

Female Behavior across Cultures

Copyright © Allyn & Bacon 2006   6

_____

_____

_____

_____

_____

_____

_____

_____

Opening the Door to Biology

❖ Nature vs. Nurture

❖ A Medical Accident

❖ Vietnam Veteran Study

7

How Females Became a Minority Group

❖ Origins of Patriarchy

  ❖ Early On, Life was Short

  ❖ Females Limited by Childbearing

  ❖ Men Became Dominant as Hunters and Warriors

  ❖ Weapons, Trade, and Knowledge gained from Contact with Others Gave Men Power

8

Gender Inequality in the U.S.

❖ Conflict Theory - Power Yields Privilege

❖ Feminism

  ❖ Biology is not Destiny

  ❖ Stratification by Gender Should Be Resisted

9

Gender Inequality in the U.S.

❖ Fighting Back: The Rise of Feminism

  ❖ First Wave - Early 1900s

  ❖ Second Wave Began 1960s

  ❖ Third Wave Emerging Now

Copyright © Allyn & Bacon 2006

Gender Inequality in the U.S.

❖ Gender Inequality in Education

❖ Gender Inequality in Health Care

Copyright © Allyn & Bacon 2006   11

Gender Inequality in the Workplace

❖ The Pay Gap

❖ The Glass Ceiling and Escalator

❖ Sexual Harassment and Worse

Copyright © Allyn & Bacon 2006   12

Gender and Violence

❖ Violence Against

Women

❖ Forcible Rape

❖ Date Rape

❖ Murder

❖ Violence in the Home

Copyright © Allyn & Bacon 2006   13

Gender and Violence

❖ Feminism and Gendered Violence

❖ Solutions

Copyright © Allyn & Bacon 2006   14

Changing Face of Politics

❖ Women Majority in Population

❖ Women Underrepresented in
   Law and Business Careers

❖ Irregular Hours Incompatible
   with Role as Mother

Copyright © Allyn & Bacon 2006

Changing Face of Politics

❖ Women Less Likely to have
  Supportive Spouse

❖ Men Reluctant to Incorporate
  Women in Decision Making

16

Glimpsing the Future
With Hope

❖ Structural Barriers Coming Down

❖ Abandoning Stereotypes

❖ New Consciousness

❖ Change in Relationships

Aging in Global Perspective

❖ Social Construction of Aging

  ❖ Tiwi vs. Abkhasians

❖ Effects of Industrialization

❖ Graying of America

  ❖ Life Expectancy

  ❖ Life span

151

Symbolic Interactionist Perspective

❖ Ageism: The Concept

❖ Shifting Meanings of Growing Old

❖ Influence of the Mass Media

Copyright © Allyn & Bacon 2006   19

Functionalist Perspective

❖ Disengagement Theory

❖ Activity Theory

❖ Continuity Theory

Copyright © Allyn & Bacon 2006   20

Conflict Perspective

❖ Social Security Legislation

❖ Intergenerational Conflict

Copyright © Allyn & Bacon 2006   21

Essentials of Sociology

Sixth Edition

**Chapter Ten: Inequalities of
Gender and Age**

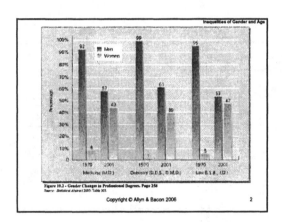

Figure 10.2 - Gender Change in Professional Degrees. Page 258
Source: Statistical Abstract 2003: Table 303.

2

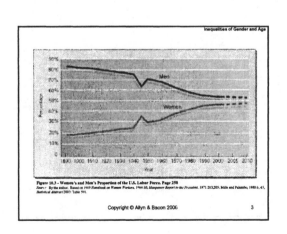

Figure 10.3 - Women's and Men's Proportion of the U.S. Labor Force. Page 258
Source: By the author. Based on 1969 Handbook on Women Workers, 1969:10; Manpower Report to the President, 1971:203,205; Mills and Palumbo, 1980:6, 45; Statistical Abstract 2003: Table 591.

3

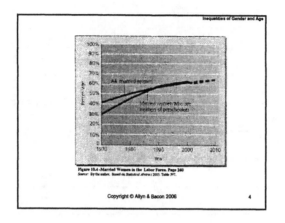

Figure 10.4 - Married Women in the Labor Force. Page 260
Source: By the author. Based on *Statistical Abstract* 2003: Table 597.

4

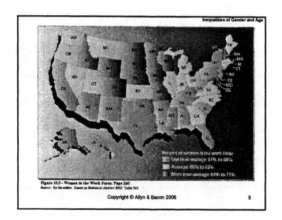

Figure 10.5 - Women in the Work Force. Page 260
Source: By the author. Based on *Statistical Abstract* 2002: Table 565.

5

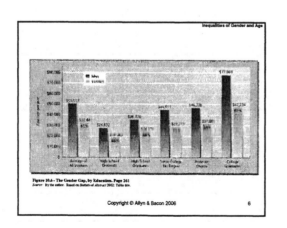

Figure 10.6 - The Gender Gap, by Education. Page 261
Source: By the author. Based on *Statistical Abstract* 2002: Table 666.

6

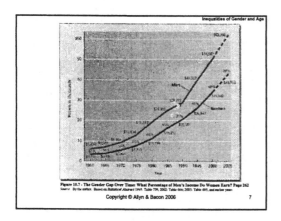

Figure 10.7 - The Gender Gap Over Time: What Percentage of Men's Income Do Women Earn? Page 262
Source: By the author. Based on Statistical Abstract 1995: Table 739; 2002: Table 666; 2003: Table 695, and earlier years.

Copyright © Allyn & Bacon 2006   7

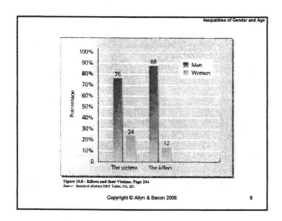

Figure 10.8 - Killers and their Victims. Page 264
Source: Statistical Abstract 2003: Tables 310, 325.

Copyright © Allyn & Bacon 2006   8

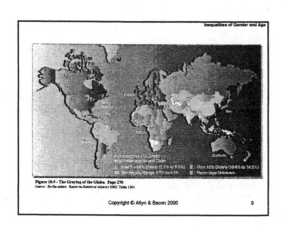

Figure 10.9 - The Graying of the Globe. Page 270
Source: By the author. Based on Statistical Abstract 2002: Table 1309.

Copyright © Allyn & Bacon 2006   9

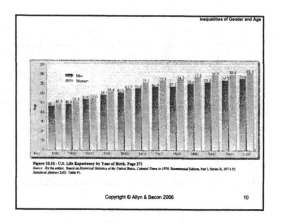

Figure 10.10 - U.S. Life Expectancy by Year of Birth. Page 271
Source By the author. Based on *Historical Statistics of the United States, Colonial Times to 1970*, Bicentennial Edition, Part 1, Series B, 107-115; *Statistical Abstract 2002*: Table 91.

Copyright © Allyn & Bacon 2006   10

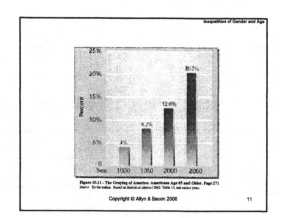

Figure 10.11 - The Graying of America: Americans Age 65 and Older. Page 271
Source By the author. Based on *Statistical Abstract 2002*: Table 13, and earlier years.

Copyright © Allyn & Bacon 2006   11

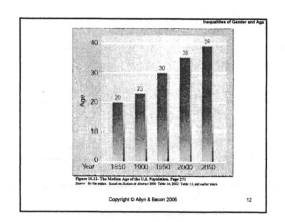

Figure 10.12 - The Median Age of the U.S. Population. Page 271
Source By the author. Based on *Statistical Abstract 2000*: Table 14; *2002*: Table 13, and earlier years.

Copyright © Allyn & Bacon 2006   12

Figure 10.13 - As Florida Goes, Go Goes the Nation: The Year 2025, Page 272
Source: By the author. Based on U.S. Bureau of the Census, 1996, U.S. Department of Commerce, PPL-47; *Statistical Abstract* 2002: Table 21.

13

_____

_____

_____

_____

_____

_____

_____

_____

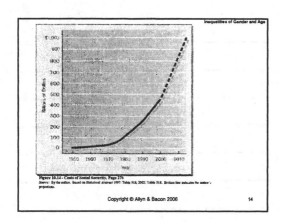

Figure 10.14 - Costs of Social Security, Page 276
Source: By the author. Based on *Statistical Abstract* 1997: Table 518; 2002: Table 518. Broken line indicates the author's projections.

14

_____

_____

_____

_____

_____

_____

_____

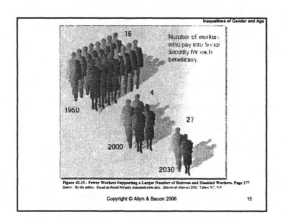

Figure 10.15 - Fewer Workers Supporting a Larger Number of Retirees and Disabled Workers, Page 277
Source: By the author. Based on Social Security Administration data. *Statistical Abstract* 2002: Tables 517, 518.

15

_____

_____

_____

_____

_____

_____

_____

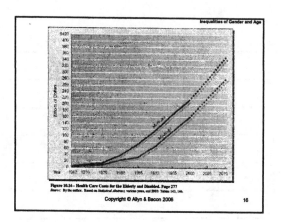

Figure 10.16 - Health Care Costs for the Elderly and Disabled. Page 277
Source: By the author. Based on *Statistical Abstract,* various years, and 2003: Tables 143, 146.

16

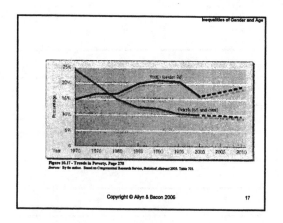

Figure 10.17 - Trends in Poverty. Page 278
Sources: By the author. Based on Congressional Research Service, *Statistical Abstract* 2003: Table 703.

17

PRACTICE TEST

1. Sex is determined by _____ characteristics and gender is determined by
   _____ characteristics.
   a. biological/social
   b. social/intellectual
   c. social/physical
   d. biological/genetic

2. Physical distinctions between males and females not directly related to reproduction, such as deeper voices in boys and broader hips in girls, are referred to as:
   a. primary sex characteristics
   b. secondary sex characteristics
   c. biological characteristics
   d. adolescent characteristics

3. The unequal access males and females have to power, prestige, and property is referred to as:
   a. class differences
   b. master status distinction
   c. gender stratification
   d. sexual harassment

4. The belief that women are better prepared biologically for "mothering" than men and that women are more sensitive to an infant's needs than a man was a position taken by feminine sociologist:
   a. Jane Addams
   b. Margaret Sanger
   c. Suellen Butler
   d. Alice Rossi

5. Females are classified as a minority group because:
   a. the number of men outnumber the number of women in society.
   b. women are discriminated against based on the physical characteristic of sex.
   c. women are less intelligent than men.
   d. they are incapable of doing the same work as a man.

6. The view that biology is not destiny and that stratification by gender is wrong and should be resisted is a concept referred to as:
   a. feminism
   b. patriarchy
   c. matriarchy
   d. fraternalism

7. Advocates of feminism
   a. are usually opposed to the policies held by suffragists.
   b. have their historic roots in strongly radical, rather than conservative, views.
   c. hold the view that biology is not destiny.
   d. focus on American society rather than Least Industrialized Nations.

8. Which of the following is *not* one of the main aspects of third wave feminism?
   a. A greater focus on the problems of women in the Least Industrialized Nations
   b. A criticism of the values that dominate work and society
   c. The removal of impediments to women's love and pleasure
   d. Changing policies on violence against women

9. According to the text, a higher percentage of women than men die after coronary bypass surgery. This is most likely attributed to women:
   a. having a weaker will to live than men.
   b. being taken less seriously by doctors when they complain of chest pains.
   c. being in surgery longer than men for the same operation.
   d. exercising less than men and not being able to deal with the stress of the operation.

10. In the U. S., full-time working women earn about what percent of what men are paid?
    a. 50   b. 35   c. 69   d. 90

11. The most invisible barrier that keeps women from reaching the executive suite in the workplace is referred to as the:
    a. glass escalator   c. glass ceiling
    b. gender barrier   d. second shift

12. The research of Christine Williams revealed that when men are hired in traditionally female positions, the men:
    a. were paid less then their female counterparts.
    b. were rejected by their female co-workers.
    c. lacked a woman's sensitivity when dealing with children or the elderly.
    d. were promoted quickly and given more desirable work assignments.

13. Which best defines sexual harassment?
    a. unwelcome sexual attention that affects a person's job or school performance
    b. gender-based job discrimination
    c. the use of sex as a means of obtaining choice jobs
    d. forced sexual activity

14. Who is the typical victim of family violence?
    a. Women   c. Children
    b. Men   d. Older adults

15. Female circumcision
    a. usually takes place when a girl reaches adolescence.
    b. must be reversed to permit sexual intercourse by having the vagina narrowed.
    c. is common in some parts of Muslim Africa, Malaysia, and Indonesia.
    d. is supported by modern feminists as a symbol of dominance for women.

16. Which of the following factors *is not* presented in the text as a reason for the long life expectancy of residents of the Abkhasian province in the Georgia republic?
    a. An absence of common Western diseases in this part of the world.
    b. A diet consisting of little meat, much fresh fruit, and wine.
    c. Lifelong physical activity.
    d. A highly developed sense of community.

17. What is the term that refers to the increasing proportion of older people in the U.S. population?
    a. Aging in a Global Perspective   c. The Graying of America
    b. Aging in a National Perspective   d. Shifting Meanings of Growing Old

18. Which statement is *least true* regarding the "graying of America"?
    a. America has the highest life expectancy of any western industrialized nation.
    b. Life expectancy in America has increased by 30 years since 1900.
    c. Today, about 13% of Americans are over 65 years of age.
    d. There are more people living in America over 65 than there are teenagers,

19. Since 1900 the length of the human life span has:
    a. increased   c. decreased
    b. remained the same   d. fluctuated with global events

20. Prejudice, discrimination, and hostility towards older people are known collectively as:
    a. ageism
    b. anti-aging
    c. age stereotyping
    d. age stigma

21. Disengagement theory and activity theory fall under the sociological perspective of:
    a. symbolic interactionism
    b. conflict theory
    c. structural functionalism
    d. neo-conflict theory

22. The addendum that anthropologist Dorothy Jerrome made to disengagement theory was:
    a. disengagement theory only applied to the young old, those between 65 and 75.
    b. disengagement theory only applies to workers in the industrial world.
    c. disengagement theory is less important during periods of economic recession.
    d. those who retire really don't disengage from roles as much as they exchange roles.

23. Which theory assumes that the more activities elderly people engage in, the more they find life satisfying?
    a. disengagement theory
    b. activity theory
    c. continuity theory
    d. conflict theory

24. The theory of aging that states people adjust to retirement by stressing some other aspect of their life, such as involvement with church, friends, lodge, or a hobby describes:
    a. neo-conflict theory
    b. subcultural theory
    c. disengagement theory
    d. continuity theory

25. The number of people who are required to pay taxes to support one person receiving the benefit of those taxes paid is called the:
    a. cost correlation
    b. dependency ratio
    c. tax coefficient
    d. social burden

PRACTICE TEST — ANSWER KEY

1. A (page 246)
2. B (page 246)
3. C (page 246)
4. D (page 248)
5. B (page 252)
6. A (page 254)
7. C (page 254)
8. D (page 255)
9. B (page 257)

10. C (page 260)
11. B (page 262)
12. D (page 262)
13. A (page 263)
14. A (page 264)
15. C (page 265
16. A (page 269)
17. C (page 270)
18. A (page 270)

19. A (page 270)
20. A (page 272)
21. C (pages 273-274)
22. D (pages 273-274)
23. B (page 274)
24. D (page 275)
25. B (page 276)

CHAPTER 11

POLITICS AND THE ECONOMY

KEY TERMS

anarchy: a condition of lawlessness or political disorder caused by the absence or collapse of governmental authority

authority: power that people accept as rightly exercised over them

capitalism: an economic system characterized by the private ownership of the means of production, the pursuit of profit, and market competition

charismatic authority: authority based on an individual's outstanding traits, which attract followers

checks and balances: the separation of powers among the three branches of U.S. government—legislative, executive and judicial—so that each is able to nullify the actions of the other two, thus preventing the domination any single branch

citizenship: the concept that birth (and residence) in a country impart basic rights

city-state: an independent city whose power radiates outward, bringing adjacent areas under its rule

coercion: illegitimate power that people do not accept as just

conspicuous consumption: Thorstein Veblen's term for a change from the Protestant ethic to an eagerness to show off wealth by the elaborate consumption of goods

convergence theory: the view that as both capitalist and socialist economic systems each adopt features of the other, a hybrid (or mixed) economic system may emerge

corporate capitalism: the domination of the economic system by giant corporations

corporation: the joint ownership of a business enterprise, whose liabilities and obligations are separate from those of the owners

democracy: a system of government in which authority derives from the people

democratic socialism: a hybrid economic system in which capitalism is mixed with state ownership

dictatorship: A form of government in which power is seized by an individual

direct democracy: a form of democracy in which voters meet together to discuss issues and make their decisions

economy: a system of distribution of goods and services

interlocking directorates: individuals serving on the board of directors in several companies

laissez-faire capitalism: unrestrained manufacture and trade (literally, "hands off" capitalism)

lobbyists: people who try to influence legislation on behalf of their clients or interest groups

market forces: the law of supply and demand

market restraints: laws and regulations govern the manufacture and sell of products

monarchy: a form of government headed by a king or queen

multinational corporation: companies that operate across national boundaries

oligarchy: a form of government in which power is held by a small group of individuals; the rule of the many by the few

pluralism: the diffusion of power among many interest groups, preventing any single group from gaining control of the government

political action committee (PAC): an organization formed by one or more special-interest groups to solicit and spend funds for the purpose of influencing legislation

power: the ability to get your way, even over the resistance of others

power elite: C. Wright Mills's term for the top leaders of U.S. corporations, military, and politics who make the nation's major decisions

rational-legal authority: authority based on law or written rules and regulations; also called *bureaucratic authority*

representative democracy: a form of democracy in which voters elect representatives to govern and make decisions on their behalf

routinization of charisma: the transfer of authority from a charismatic figure to either a traditional or a rational-legal form of authority

socialism: an economic system characterized by the public ownership of the means of production, central planning, and the distribution of goods without a profit motive

special-interest group: people who share views on a particular issue and can be mobilized for political action

state: the political entity that claims a monopoly on the use of violence within a territory

stockholders' revolt: the refusal of a corporation's stockholders to rubber-stamp decisions made by its managers

subsistence economy: the type of economy in which human groups live off the land with little or no surplus

totalitarianism: a form of government that exerts almost total control over the people

traditional authority: authority based on custom

universal citizenship: the idea that everyone has the same basic rights by virtue of being born in a country (or by immigrating and becoming a naturalized citizen)

voter apathy: indifference and inaction with respect to the political process

welfare (or state) capitalism: an economic system in which individual own the means of production but the state regulates many economic activities for the welfare of the population

KEY PEOPLE

Daniel Bell: Bell identified six characteristic of the postindustrial society.

Peter Berger: Berger argued that violence is the ultimate foundation of any political order.

William Domhoff: Like Mills, Domhoff saw that power resides in an elite, which he referred to as the ruling class. He focused on the top one percent of Americans who belong to the super rich.

Bennett Harrison and Barry Bluestone: These social analysts have used the expression "the great American U-turn" to describe the stagnating/declining standard of living of many Americans today.

C.Wright Mills: Mills suggested that power resides in the hands of an elite made up of the top leaders of the largest corporations, the most powerful generals of the armed forces, and certain elite politicians.

Michael Useem: Using a conflict perspective, Useem studied the activities of the "inner circle" of corporate executives.

Thorstein Veblen: Veblen created the term "conspicuous consumption" to refer to the eagerness to show off one's wealth through the elaborate consumption of material goods.

Max Weber: Weber identified three different types of authority: traditional, rational-legal, and charismatic.

Essentials of Sociology

Sixth Edition

Chapter Eleven: Politics and the
Economy

This multimedia product and its contents are protected under copyright law. The following are prohibited by law: any public performance or display, including transmission of any image over a network; preparation of any derivative work, including the extraction, in whole or in part, of any images; any rental, lease, or lending of the program.

Chapter Overview

❖ Power, Authority, and Violence

❖ Types of Government

❖ The U.S. Political System

❖ Who Rules the United States?

❖ The Transformation of Economic Systems

❖ World Economic Systems

❖ Capitalism in a Global Economy

Copyright © Allyn & Bacon 2006

2

Power, Authority, and Violence

❖ Power - Ability to Get Your Way

❖ Authority - Legitimate Power

❖ Coercion - Illegitimate Power

Copyright © Allyn & Bacon 2006

3

Power, Authority, and Violence

❖ Authority and Legitimate Violence

❖ Traditional Authority

  ❖Authority Based on Custom

❖ Rational-Legal Authority

  ❖Authority Based on Written Rules

Copyright © Allyn & Bacon 2006   4

Power, Authority, and Violence

❖ Charismatic Authority

  ❖Authority Freely and Graciously Given

  ❖Threat Posed by Charismatic Leaders

❖ Transfer of Authority

  ❖Orderly From one Leader to Another

Copyright © Allyn & Bacon 2006   5

Types of Governments

❖ Monarchies

❖ Democracies

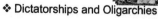

  ❖Direct

  ❖Representative

❖ Dictatorships and Oligarchies

  ❖Totalitarianism

Copyright © Allyn & Bacon 2006   6

U.S. Political System

❖ Political Parties and Elections

  ❖ Primaries and Elections

  ❖ Democrats, Republicans, and Third Parties

7

Voting Patterns

❖ Non-Hispanic Whites Most Likely to Vote

❖ African Americans Next Most Likely

❖ Latinos Least Likely to Vote

8

Voting Patterns

❖ Social Integration

❖ Alienation and Apathy

❖ Gender and Racial-Ethnic Gap in Voting

9

Lobbyists and Special Interests

❖ Special Interest Groups are People Who Think Alike on a Particular Issue and Mobilize for Political Action

❖ Lobbyist are People Paid to Influence Legislation

Copyright © Allyn & Bacon 2006

10

PACs in U.S. Elections

❖ PACs Bankroll Lobbyists and Legislators

❖ PAC Money Buys Votes

❖ Most PACs Stand for Financial Interests of Specific Groups

Copyright © Allyn & Bacon 2006

11

Who Rules the U.S.?

❖ Functionalist Perspective: Pluralism

❖ Protection from Anarchy

❖ Diffusion of Power Among Many

❖ Checks and Balances

Copyright © Allyn & Bacon 2006

12

168

Who Rules the U.S.?

❖ Conflict Perspective: The Power Elite

    ❖Ruling Class

    ❖Top Business, Political, and Military Leaders

  13

_____
_____
_____
_____
_____
_____

War and Terrorism

❖ Three Essential Conditions of War

    ❖A Cultural Tradition

    ❖An Antagonistic Situation

    ❖A fuel that Heats the Antagonistic Situation

  14

_____
_____
_____
_____
_____
_____

War and Terrorism

❖ Why do Nations go to

War?

    ❖Revenge

    ❖Power

    ❖Prestige

    ❖Unity

    ❖Positions

    ❖Ethnicity

    ❖Beliefs

  15

_____
_____
_____
_____
_____
_____

War and Dehumanization

❖ Moral Cost

❖ Reducing People to Objects

❖ Breeds Callousness and Cruelty

❖ Characterization of Struggle Between Good and Evil

❖ Terrorism - Use of Violence to Create Fear

Copyright © Allyn & Bacon 2006

16

The Transformation of Economic Systems

❖ Preindustrial Societies: Birth of Inequality

  ❖ Hunting and Gathering Societies

  ❖ Pastoral and Horticultural Societies

  ❖ Agricultural Societies

❖ Increasing Social and Economic Inequalities

Copyright © Allyn & Bacon 2006

17

The Transformation of Economic Systems

❖ Industrial Societies: Birth of the Machine

  ❖ Brought Previously Unseen Surpluses

  ❖ Factories Exploited Labor

  ❖ More Efficient Machines Led to Conspicuous Consumption

Copyright © Allyn & Bacon 2006

The Transformation of Economic Systems

❖ Postindustrial Societies: Birth of Information Age

- ◆ Service Sector
- ◆ Vast Surplus of Goods
- ◆ Extensive Trade among Nations
- ◆ Wider Variety and Quantity of Goods
- ◆ Information Explosion
- ◆ Global Village

Copyright © Allyn & Bacon 2006   19

_____

_____

_____

_____

_____

_____

_____

The Transformation of Economic Systems

❖ Bioeconomic Societies: Merger of Biology and Economics

❖ We May Be on the Verge of New Type of Society

❖ Likely to Lead to Even Greater Inequalities

Copyright © Allyn & Bacon 2006   20

_____

_____

_____

_____

_____

_____

_____

Ominous Trends in the United States

❖ Reduction in Jobs and Benefits

❖ Stagnant and Shrinking

Paychecks

❖ Income Inequalities

Copyright © Allyn & Bacon 2006   21

_____

_____

_____

_____

_____

_____

_____

World Economic Systems

❖ Capitalism

  ❖ Private Ownership of Means of Production

  ❖ Market Competition

  ❖ Pursuit of Profit

❖ Laissez-Faire Capitalism

❖ Welfare or State Capitalism

❖ Market Restraints

Copyright © Allyn & Bacon 2006

World Economic Systems

❖ Socialism

  ❖ Public Ownership of Means of Production

  ❖ Central Planning

  ❖ Distribution of Goods without Profit Motive

❖ Needs Decided by Central Committee

❖ Designed to Eliminate Competition

❖ Everyone Works for the Government

Copyright © Allyn & Bacon 2006   23

Ideologies of Capitalism and Socialism

❖ Capitalists

  ❖ Market Prices Should Determine Products and Prices

  ❖ Profits are Good for Humanity

  ❖ Society Benefits from More Supply and Cheaper Prices

Copyright © Allyn & Bacon 2006   24

Ideologies of Capitalism and Socialism

❖ Socialists

  ❖ Profit is Immoral

  ❖ Item's Value Based on the Work that Went Into It

  ❖ Government Protects Workers from Exploitation

Copyright © Allyn & Bacon 2006   25

_____

_____

_____

_____

_____

_____

_____

Criticisms of Capitalism and Socialism

❖ Capitalism

  ❖ Leads to Social Inequality

  ❖ Tiny Top Layer Exploits Vast Bottom Layer

  ❖ Few Who Own the Means of Production Reap Huge Profits

Copyright © Allyn & Bacon 2006   26

_____

_____

_____

_____

_____

_____

_____

Criticisms of Capitalism and Socialism

❖ Socialism

  ❖ Does not Respect Individual Rights

  ❖ Others Control People's Lives

  ❖ Give Everyone an Equal Chance to be Poor

Copyright © Allyn & Bacon 2006   27

_____

_____

_____

_____

_____

_____

_____

Convergence of Capitalism and Socialism

❖ Convergence Theory

❖ Hybrid or Mixed Economy

❖ Changes in China and Russia

❖ Changes in America

28

Capitalism in a Global Economy

❖ Corporate Capitalism
   ❖ Business Treated as a Person
   ❖ Separation of Ownership and Management

❖ Stockholders' Revolt

❖ Interlocking Directorates

29

Multinational Corporations

❖ Corporations have Outgrown National Boundaries

❖ Become More Detached from Interests and Values of Country of Origin

❖ Have Become a Powerful Political Force

30

A New World Order?

❖ World's Nations Embracing Capitalism

❖ Perhaps Consequence will be World Peace

❖ Expansion of Multinationals may Stimulate Trade Agreements

31

_____

_____

_____

_____

_____

_____

_____

Essentials of Sociology
Sixth Edition

Chapter Eleven: Politics and the Economy

This multimedia product and its contents are protected under copyright law. The following are prohibited by law: any public performance or display, including transmission of any image over a network; preparation of any derivative work, including the extraction, in whole or in part, of any images; any rental, lease, or lending of the program.

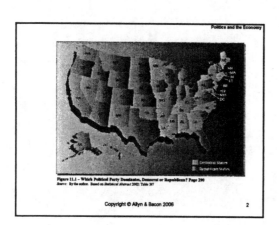

Figure 11.1 – Which Political Party Dominates, Democrat or Republican? Page 290
Source: By the author. Based on Statistical Abstract 2002: Table 307

Copyright © Allyn & Bacon 2006   2

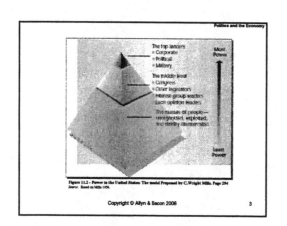

The top leaders
- Corporate
- Political
- Military

The middle level
- Congress
- Other legislators
- Interest-group leaders
- Local opinion leaders

The masses of people—
unorganized, exploited,
and mostly disinterested

Most Power

Least Power

Figure 11.2 – Power in the United States: The model Proposed by C.Wright Mills. Page 294
Source: Based on Mills 1956.

Copyright © Allyn & Bacon 2006   3

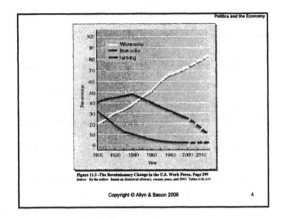

Figure 11.3 -The Revolutionary Change in the U.S. Work Force. Page 399
Source: By the author. Based on Statistical Abstract, various years, and 2003: Tables 618, 619.

4

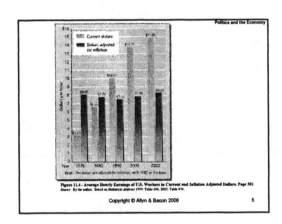

Figure 11.4 - Average Hourly Earnings of U.S. Workers in Current and Inflation Adjusted Dollars. Page 361
Source: By the author. Based on Statistical Abstract 1999: Table 698; 2003: Table 616.

5

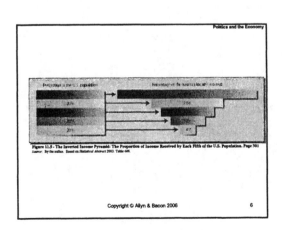

Figure 11.5 - The Inverted Income Pyramid: The Proportion of Income Received by Each Fifth of the U.S. Population. Page 361
Source: By the author. Based on Statistical Abstract 2003: Table 680.

6

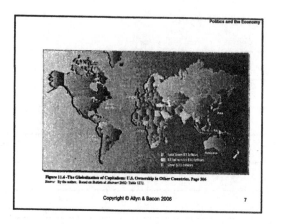

Figure 11.6 - The Globalization of Capitalism: U.S. Ownership in Other Countries. Page 306
Source By the author. Based on *Statistical Abstract* 2002: Table 1272.

7

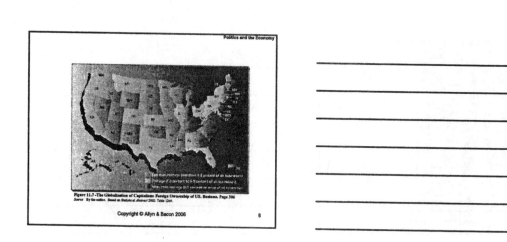

Figure 11.7 - The Globalization of Capitalism: Foreign Ownership of U.S. Business. Page 306
Source By the author. Based on *Statistical Abstract* 2002: Table 1269.

8

1. Jerome is the leader of the local gang. Several other gang members have tried to replace him but have failed. If Jerome wants the gang to pursue a particular assignment, they do, even though many members of the gang may oppose the effort. Jerome is not a particularly good looking or well liked leader, but he has been able to remain in command and the gang follows his direction. Based upon this description, the quality Jerome appears to have mastered is:
   a. charisma
   b. traditional authority
   c. expertise
   d. power

2. The opposite of authority, which is defined as legitimate power, would be:
   a. coercion   b. competition   c. tradition   d. coalescence

3. Authority that is based on custom, such as leadership succession in tribes is referred to as:
   a. rational-legal authority
   b. traditional authority
   c. de facto authority
   d. de jure authority

4. The President of the United States rules by
   a. charismatic authority.
   b. political authority.
   c. rational-legal authority.
   d. traditional authority.

5. Joan of Arc, Fidel Castro, and Adolph Hitler all had something in common which was:
   a. they were all leaders of their respective nations.
   b. they all rose to greatness through the use of rational-legal authority.
   c. they had large followings based on their charismatic charm.
   d. they were all members of the upper class.

6. John F. Kennedy is one of those few leaders who combined which two types of authority?
   a. coercion, legal-rational
   b. legal-rational, charismatic
   c. charismatic, traditional
   d. illegitimate, legal-rational

7. Which statement is *least true* regarding charismatic authority?
   a. Charismatic leaders pose a threat to the established political system.
   b. Charismatic leaders tend to lead their followers based on personal inclination.
   c. Charismatic leaders are often opposed by traditional and rational-legal authorities.
   d. Charismatic leaders pose little threat to established leaders because they are too informal,

8. During the feudal period, the rule of England under the reign of a king and queen would be classified as which type of government?
   a. limited democracy
   b. representative democracy
   c. monarchy
   d. dictatorship

9. The word *democracy* comes from two _____ words; *demos* meaning _____ and *kratos* meaning power.
   a. Latin/freedom
   b. Greek/common people
   c. German/state
   d. Old English/democratic

10. Nazi Germany, with its Gestapo, secret police force, and spies who watched everyone, was a good example of:
    a. totalitarianism
    b. representative democracy
    c. ecclesia
    d. nation-state

11. The person most likely to vote in an American election is the one who possesses which set of characteristics?
    a. a young, Latino college graduate entering the work force
    b. a recently retired, white college professor
    c. a middle aged American gainfully employed as a brick layer
    d. an older African American engineer working for NASA

12. People who form a group that thinks alike on a particular issue and who can be mobilized for political action, are referred to as a/an:
    a. third party
    b. special-interest group
    c. political auxiliary
    d. legislative cohort

13. A functionalist approach to government where there is a diffusion of power among many interest groups, preventing any one group from gaining control of the government is referred to as:
    a. pluralism
    b. multi-partisan politics
    c. the electoral college
    d. political action committee

14. According to C. Wright Mills, the most important decisions of the government are made by top leaders of the largest corporations, certain elite politicians, and a handful of others known as:
    a. the Group of Seven
    b. the Power Elite
    c. the Joint Chiefs of Staff
    d. Stargate One

15. Which one of the following is not one of Timasheff's essential conditions of war?
    a. An antagonistic situation in which two or more states confront incompatible objectives
    b. A cultural tradition of war
    c. A "fuel" that heats the antagonistic situation so that politicians move from thinking about war to waging it
    d. Dehumanization and a tendency for prolonged conflicts between good and evil

16. The use of violence to create fear to try to bring about political objectives, which is most often used by a group that is politically weaker than its opponent is:
    a. dehumanization
    b. suicide
    c. terrorism
    d. propaganda

17. Which statement is *least true* regarding terrorism?
    a. It is the use of violence to create fear in an effort to bring about political objectives.
    b. It includes the use of suicide terrorism that shocks the world and captures headlines.
    c. It is relatively new to world history, being born by Middle Eastern groups in the 1970's.
    d. It is often used by a group that is politically weaker than its opponent.

18. A system of producing goods and services is referred to as:
    a. politics
    b. compurgation
    c. economy
    d. modernization

19. Which of the following societies was the most likely to survive on a subsistence economy?
    a. agricultural society
    b. horticultural society
    c. pastoral society
    d. hunting and gathering society

20. Which sociologists coined the term conspicuous consumption?
    a. Thorstein Veblen
    b. C. Wright Mills
    c. William Domoff
    d. Immanuel Wallerstein

21. The richest fifth of Americans earn _____ of the entire country's income, while only _____go to the poorest fifth.
    a. 20 percent/20 percent
    b. 35 percent/10 percent
    c. 47 percent/4 percent
    d. 98 percent/1 percent

22. The current form of U.S. capitalism where private citizens own the means of production and pursue profits within a vast system of laws designed to protect the welfare of the population is referred to as welfare capitalism or:
    a. state capitalism
    b. laissez-faire capitalism
    c. democratic capitalism
    d. free market capitalism

23. The current economic system in the United States is
    a. laissez-faire capitalism.
    b. unrestrained capitalism.
    c. welfare capitalism.
    d. market capitalism.

24. Which of the following is a characteristic of a socialist economy?
    a. central planning
    b. pursuit of profits
    c. monopolistic goals for private corporations
    d. private ownership

25. Which two countries are examples of democratic socialism, which is also known as welfare socialism?
    a. Canada and Mexico
    b. China and Russia
    c. Denmark and Sweden
    d. Japan and Germany

PRACTICE TEST — ANSWER KEY

1. D (page 284)
2. A (page 284)
3. B (page 284)
4. C (page 285)
5. C (page 285)
6. B (page 285)
7. D (page 285)
8. C (page 285)
9. B (page 287)

10. A (page 289)
11. B (page 290)
12. B (page 292)
13. A (page 293)
14. B (page 294)
15. D (page 295)
16. C (page 296)
17. C (page 296)
18. C (page 298)

19. D (page 298)
20. A (page 298)
21. C (page 301)
22. A (page 302)
23. C (page 302)
24. A (page 303)
25. C (page 303)

CHAPTER 12

MARRIAGE AND FAMILY

KEY TERMS

bilateral system: a system of reckoning descent that counts both the mother's and the father's side

blended family: a family whose members were once part of other families

cohabitation: unmarried people living together in a sexual relationship

empty nest: a married couple's domestic situation after the last child has left home

endogamy: the practice of marrying within one's group

exogamy: the practice of marrying outside one's group

extended family: a nuclear family plus other relatives, such as grandparents, uncles, aunts, and cousins, who live together

family: two or more people who consider themselves related by blood, marriage, or adoption.

family of orientation: the family in which a person grows up

family of procreation: the family formed when a couple's first child is born

homogamy: the tendency of people with similar characteristics to marry one another

household: all persons who occupy the same housing unit

incest taboo: rules specifying the degrees of kinship that prohibit sex or marriage

machismo: an emphasis on male strength and dominance

marriage: a group's approved mating arrangements, usually marked by a ritual of some sort

matriarchy: a society or group in which authority is vested in women

matrilineal system: a system of reckoning descent that counts only the mother's side

nuclear family: a family consisting of a husband, wife, and child(ren)

patriarchy: a society or group n which authority is vested in men

patrilineal system: a system of reckoning descent that counts only the father's side

polyandry: a marriage in which a woman has more than one husband

polygyny: a marriage in which a man has more than one wife

romantic love: feelings of erotic attraction accompanied by an idealization of the other

serial fatherhood: a pattern of parenting in which a father, after divorce, reduces contact with his own children, serves as a father to the children of the woman he marries or lives with, then ignores them after moving in with or marrying another woman; this pattern repeats

system of descent: how kinship is traced over the generations

KEY PEOPLE

Philip Blumstein and Pepper Schwartz: These two sociologists interviewed same-sex couples and found their main struggles were the same ones facing heterosexual couples.

Urie Bronfenbrenner: This sociologist studied the impact of divorce on children and found that children adjust better if there is a second adult who can be counted on for support.

Larry Bumpass: Bumpass noted that the average age of first marriage has not changed that much, if cohabitation is included in the picture.

Andrew Cherlin: Cherlin notes that our society has not yet developed adequate norms for remarriage.

Donald Dutton and Arthur Aron: These researchers compared the sexual arousal levels of men who are in dangerous situations with men in safe situations and found that the former were more sexually aroused than the latter.

Kathleen Gerson: Gerson found that there are different reasons why some couples choose not to have children—weak marriages, expenses associated with raising children, diminished career opportunities.

Alex Heckert, Thomas Nowak and Kay Snyder: These researchers did secondary analysis of data gathered on a nationally representative sample and found that divorce increases when women earn more than their husbands, the wife's health is poorer than her husband's, or the wife does less housework.

Arlie Hochschild: Hochschild conducted research on families in which both parents are employed full-time in order to find out how household tasks are divided up. She found that women did more of the housework than their husbands, resulting in women putting in a *second shift* at home after their workday has ended.

William Jankowiak and Edward Fischer: These anthropologists surveyed date on 166 societies and found that the majority of them contained the ideal of romantic love.

Melvin Kohn: Kohn studied social class differences in child-rearing.

Jeanette & Robert Lauer: These sociologists interviewed 351 couples who had been married fifteen years and longer in order to find out what makes a marriage successful.

Lillian Rubin: Rubin compared working and middle class couples and found the key to how well the couple adjusts to the arrival of children is social class. Rubin also interviewed both career women and homemakers found that the notion of the "empty-nest" as a difficult time for women is largely a myth and that most women's satisfaction increased when the last child left home.

Diana Russell: Russell found that incest victims who experience the most difficulty are those who have been victimized the most often, over longer periods of time, and whose incest was "more intrusive."

Nicholas Stinnett: Stinnett studied 660 families from all regions of the U.S. and parts of South American in order to find out what the characteristics of happy families are.

Murray Straus: this sociologist has studied domestic violence and found that, while husbands and wives are equally likely to attack one another, men inflict more damage on women than the reverse.

Bob Suzuki: This sociologist studied Chinese-American and Japanese-American families and identified several distinctive characteristics of this type of family.

Martin Whyte: Whyte interviewed married women in the greater Detroit area and found that marital satisfaction tended to decrease with the birth of a child.

Essentials of Sociology
Sixth Edition

Chapter Twelve: Marriage and Family

This multimedia product and its contents are protected under copyright law. The following are prohibited by law: any public performance or display, including transmission of any image over a network; preparation of any derivative work, including the extraction, in whole or in part, of any images; any rental, lease, or lending of the program.

Chapter Overview

- ❖ Marriage and Family in Global Perspective
- ❖ Marriage and Family in Theoretical Perspective
- ❖ The Family Life Cycle
- ❖ Diversity in U.S. Families

- ❖ Trends in U.S. Families
- ❖ Divorce and Remarriage
- ❖ Two Sides of Family Life
- ❖ The Future of Marriage and Family

Copyright © Allyn & Bacon 2006

2

What is a Family?

- ❖ Western - One Woman, Man, and Children
- ❖ Other Cultures Polygamy and Polyandry
- ❖ Approved Group into Which a Child is Born?

Copyright © Allyn & Bacon 2006

3

Family Defined

"A family consists of people who consider

themselves related by blood, marriage, or

adoption."

4

Common Cultural Themes

❖ Families Establish Patterns of...

  ❖Mate Selection

  ❖Descent

  ❖Inheritance

  ❖Authority

5

Marriage and Family

Functionalist Perspective

❖ Economic Production

❖ Socialization of Children

❖ Care of Sick and Aged

Marriage and Family
Functionalist Perspective

❖ Recreation

❖ Sexual Control

❖ Reproduction

Copyright © Allyn & Bacon 2006   7

Marriage and Family
Functionalist Perspective

❖ Functions of Incest and Taboo

❖ Isolation and Emotional Overload

Copyright © Allyn & Bacon 2006   8

Marriage and Family
Conflict Perspective

❖ Gender and Power

  ❖ Power Struggle over Housework

  ❖ Working Wives and the "Second Shift"

Copyright © Allyn & Bacon 2006   9

Marriage and Family

Symbolic Interactionist Perspective

❖ Gender and Housework

  ❖ More Equally Paid, More Equal Housework

  ❖ Laid Off Men Do Less Housework

  ❖ Men Who Earn Less than Wives Do Least

  Housework

Copyright © Allyn & Bacon 2006   10

The Family Life Cycle

❖ Love and Courtship in Global

  Perspective

❖ Romantic Love

❖ Marriage Copyright © Allyn & Bacon 2006   11

The Family Life Cycle

❖ Child Rearing

  ❖ Married Couples and Single Mothers

  ❖ Day Care

  ❖ Nannies

  ❖ Social Class

Copyright © Allyn & Bacon 2006   12

The Family Life Cycle

❖ Family in Later Life

    ❖ The Empty Nest

    ❖ "Boomerang" Children

    ❖ Widowhood

Copyright © Allyn & Bacon 2006   13

Diversity in U.S. Families

❖ African American Families

❖ Latino Families

❖ Asian Families

❖ Native American Families

Copyright © Allyn & Bacon 2006   14

Diversity in U.S. Families

❖ One-Parent Families

❖ Families without Children

❖ Blended Families

❖ Gay and Lesbian Families

Copyright © Allyn & Bacon 2006   15

Trends in U.S. Families

❖ Postponing Marriage and Childbirth

❖ Cohabitation

❖ Unmarried Mothers

❖ Grandparents as Parents

❖ The Sandwich Generation and Elder Care

Copyright © Allyn & Bacon 2006   16

Divorce and Remarriage

❖ Problems in Measuring Divorce

❖ Children of Divorce

❖ Absent Fathers and Serial Fatherhood

❖ Ex-Spouses

❖ Remarriage

Copyright © Allyn & Bacon 2006   17

Two Sides of Family Life

❖ The Dark Side

　❖ Battering

　❖ Child Abuse

　❖ Incest

Copyright © Allyn & Bacon 2006   18

Two Sides of Family Life

❖ The Bright Side - Successful Marriages

  ❖ Spouse is Best Friend

  ❖ Like Spouse as Person

  ❖ Think Marriage is Long-Term Commitment

  ❖ Believe Marriage is Sacred

Copyright © Allyn & Bacon 2006   19

Two Sides of Family Life

❖ The Bright Side - Successful Marriages

  ❖ Agree with Spouse Aims and Goals

  ❖ Believe Spouse Grown More Interesting

  ❖ Want Relationship to Succeed

  ❖ Laugh Together

Copyright © Allyn & Bacon 2006   20

Symbolic Interactionism and Misuse of Statistics

❖ Students' Concerns for Own Marriages

❖ Divorce Rates are Overall Rates

❖ Divorce Rates Unrelated to Individual Marriages

❖ Our Chances Depend on Our Situations

Copyright © Allyn & Bacon 2006   21

The Future of Marriage and Family

❖ No Danger of Becoming a Relic

❖ Cohabitation, Single Mothers, Age at

   Marriage, Grandparents as Parents

   will Increase

❖ Equality in Marriage not on Horizon

22

_____

_____

_____

_____

_____

_____

_____

Essentials of Sociology

Sixth Edition

Chapter Twelve: Marriage and Family

This multimedia product and its contents are protected under copyright law. The following are prohibited by law: any public performance or display, including transmission of any image over a network; preparation of any derivative work, including the extraction, in whole or in part, of any images; any rental, lease, or lending of the program.

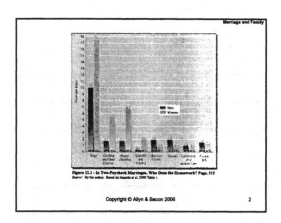

Figure 12.1 – In Two-Paycheck Marriages, Who Does the Housework? Page. 315
Source: By the author. Based on Bianchi et al. 2000 Table 1.

Copyright © Allyn & Bacon 2006   2

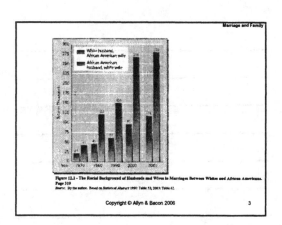

White husband, African American wife

African American husband, white wife

Figure 12.2 – The Racial Background of Husbands and Wives in Marriages Between Whites and African Americans. Page 319
Source: By the author. Based on Statistical Abstract 1990: Table 53, 2003: Table 62.

Copyright © Allyn & Bacon 2006   3

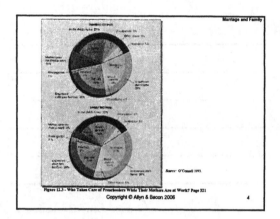

Marriage and Family

Figure 12.3 - Who Takes Care of Preschoolers While Their Mothers Are at Work? Page 321

Copyright © Allyn & Bacon 2006   4

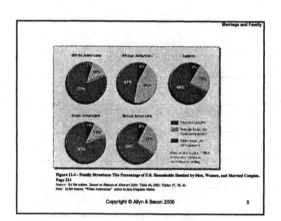

Marriage and Family

Figure 12.4 - Family Structure The Percentage of U.S. Households Headed by Men, Women, and Married Couples. Page 324

Source: By the author. Based on *Statistical Abstract* 2000: Table 44; 2002: Tables 37, 38, 40.

Note: In the source, "White Americans" refers to non-Hispanic whites.

Copyright © Allyn & Bacon 2006   5

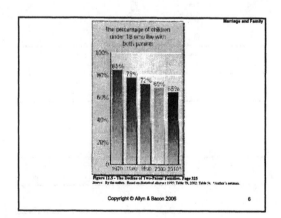

Marriage and Family

Figure 12.5 - The Decline of Two-Parent Families. Page 325

Source: By the author. Based on *Statistical Abstract* 1995: Table 79; 2002: Table 54. *Author's estimate.

Copyright © Allyn & Bacon 2006   6

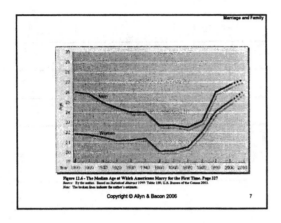

Figure 12.6 - The Median Age at Which Americans Marry for the First Time. Page 327
Source: By the author. Based on *Statistical Abstract* 1999: Table 159; U.S. Bureau of the Census 2003.
Note: The broken lines indicate the author's estimate.

7

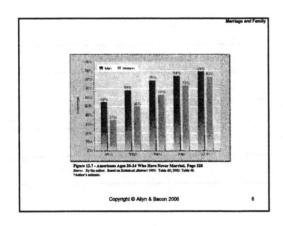

Figure 12.7 - Americans Ages 20-34 Who Have Never Married. Page 328
Source: By the author. Based on *Statistical Abstract* 1995: Table 60; 2002: Table 48.
*Author's estimate.

8

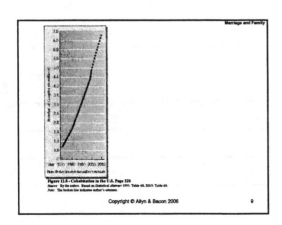

Figure 12.8 - Cohabitation in the U.S. Page 328
Source: By the author. Based on *Statistical Abstract* 1995: Table 60, 2003: Table 69.
Note: The broken line indicates author's estimate.

9

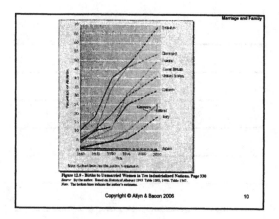

Figure 12.9 - Births to Unmarried Women in Ten Industrialized Nations. Page 330
Source: By the author. Based on *Statistical Abstract* 1993 Table 1303; 1998, Table 1347.
Note: The broken lines indicate the author's estimates.

10

Figure 12.10 - The "Where" of U.S. Divorce. Page 331
Source: By the author. Based on *Statistical Abstract* 2002; Table 111, and earlier editions.
Note: Data for California, Colorado, Indiana, and Louisiana, based on earlier editions, have been decreased by the average decrease in U.S. divorce.

11

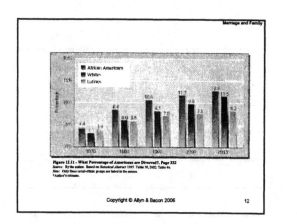

Figure 12.11 - What Percentage of Americans are Divorced?. Page 332
Source: By the author. Based on *Statistical Abstract* 1995 Table 58; 2002; Table 46.
Note: Only these racial-ethnic groups are listed in the source.
*Author's estimate.

12

196

Marriage and Family

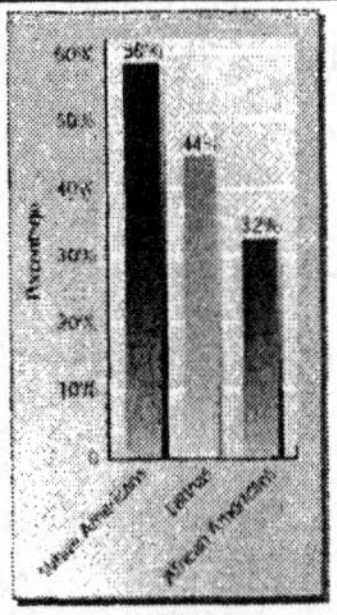

Figure 12.12 - The Probability that Divorced Women Will Remarry in Five Years. Page 335
Source: By the author. Based on Bramlett and Mosher 2002.
Note: Only these groups are listed in the source.

13

PRACTICE TEST

1. Which statement is *least true* regarding the concept of family?
   a. It consists of people who consider themselves related by blood, marriage, or adoption.
   b. Family can include more than one wife for the husband.
   c. Because of tradition, family is relatively simple to define and consistent worldwide.
   d. Same sex marriages are legal in Denmark, Norway, Sweden, and Holland.

2. Which of the following refers to the marriage of one woman to several men?
   a. polyandry   c. polygyny
   b. polygamy   d. bigamy

3. The Family of _____ is the family in which an individual grows up.
   a. Procreation   b. Recreation   c. Orientation   d. Custom

4. Which statement is *least true* regarding mate selection and mate selection practices?
   a. The incest taboo is an example of exogamy.
   b. Norms of endogamy require people to marry outside their own group.
   c. Norms of endogamy are the most practiced mating arrangement.
   d. In most society norms of mate selection are informal.

5. In a bilateral system of descent:
   a. descent is traced only on the father's side.
   b. children are related to both their father's side of the family and their mother's side.
   c. descent is traced only on the mother's side.
   d. women retain their maiden name in marriage.

6. Naming patterns that occur during marriage and following the birth of children most reflect:
   a. patriarchy   b. matriarchy   c. egalitarianism   d. functionalism

7. The fact that family provides economic production, socialization of children, recreation, sexual control, and reproduction support the _____ perspective of family.
   a. Functionalist   c. Symbolic Interactionist
   b. Conflict   d. Neo-Conflict

8. The term used by Arlie Hochschild to describe a woman's role as wife and mother when she returns from a regular job outside the home is:
   a. the sandwich generation.   c. the equal rights amendment
   b. women's revolution.   d. the second shift

9. Hochschild's "strategy of resistance" that men use to avoid housework characterized by forgetting grocery shopping lists and where kitchen utensils may be stored is:
   a. waiting it out.   c. substitute offering
   b. needs reduction   d. playing dumb

10. Under the symbolic interactionist perspective of marriage and family, when a husband is laid off:
    a. he does more of the housework at his wife's insistence.
    b. he does more housework voluntarily to fill his free time.
    c. he does less of the housework than ever before.
    d. he maintains a similar level of housework that he did before being laid off.

11. About what percent of Americans marry someone from their own racial background?
    a. 94   b. 84   c. 73   d. 65

12. Rubin's research showed that when the last child leaves home:
    a. a woman falls into deep depression because of the "empty nest syndrome."
    b. that couples often divorce because there is no longer anything to keep them together.
    c. men are more likely to become unfaithful in the marital relationship.
    d. a woman's level of marital satisfaction increases because it's a big relief to be childfree.

13. The key ingredient that over shadows all other factors in determining family life style, values, and beliefs is:
    a. level of education   c. intellectual ability of the parents
    b. race   d. social class

14. Jodi's mother has a close friend who has shared in Jodi's rearing and development. Jodi respectfully refers to her mother's friend as "Aunt Sally". Sally qualifies as being Jodi's:
    a. affinal kin   c. fictive kin
    b. consanguinal kin   d. platonic kin

15. The marriage squeeze refers to:
    a. the imbalance of fewer eligible women for eligible men in the marriage market.
    b. the imbalance of fewer eligible men for eligible women in the marriage market.
    c. the trend for younger people to marry who are ill prepared emotionally and financially.
    d. families who need to take care of children at home as well as their aging parents.

16. In regard to one-parent families:
    a. the number of one-parent families in the US has tripled since 1970.
    b. one of the major reasons for this phenomenon is a high divorce rate.
    c. one of the major reasons for this phenomenon is births to unmarried women.
    d. most one-parent families are headed by women.

17. In families where both the husband and wife are gainfully employed and there are no children in the home by choice, the couples are referred to as:
    a. nerds   b. dinks   c. yuppies   d. open marriages

18. Families, whose members were once part of other families, such as one single parent marrying another single parent, are called:
    a. extended families   c. blended families
    b. one-parent families   d. empty nests

19. The first country to legalize marriage between people of the same sex was:
    a. Holland   b. Norway   c. France   d. Denmark

20. Cohabitation is _____ today than it was 30 years ago.
    a. far less common   c. not any more common
    b. ten times more common   d. less social acceptable

21. People who find themselves caring for their children and their own aging parents are part of:
    a. a skipped generation family   c. an unhappy household
    b. the sandwich generation   d. a second shift

22. The divorce rate in the United States is:
    a. 2 percent
    b. 10 percent
    c. 50 percent
    d. 98 percent

23. Which of the following is *least true* about children of divorce:
    a. Less likely to complete high school
    b. Less likely to be juvenile delinquents
    c. Less likely to attend college
    d. Less likely to graduate from college

24. Serial Fatherhood refers to:
    a. men who father babies to multiple women without the benefit of marriage.
    b. a man adopting the children born to a woman during her previous marriage.
    c. divorced fathers spending more time with their new wife's children rather than their own.
    d. men who deny paternity responsibility because they are legally married to someone else.

25. Of those marriages found to be "unhappy" but in which the couples were staying together, all of the following were reasons, according to Lauer, EXCEPT
    a. thinking of their spouse as their best friend.
    b. religious reasons.
    c. family tradition reasons.
    d. for the sake of the children.

PRACTICE TEST — ANSWER KEY

1. C (page 312)
2. A (page 312)
3. C (pages 312-313)
4. B (page 313)
5. B (page 313)
6. A (page 313)
7. A (page 314)
8. D (page 316)
9. D (page 316)

10. C (page 317)
11. A (page 319)
12. D (page 322)
13. D (page 320)
14. C (page 323)
15. B (page 323)
16. D (page 325)
17. B (page 326)
18. C (page 326)

19. D (page 326)
20. B (page 327)
21. B (page 330)
22. A (page 331)
23. B (page 332)
24. C (page 334)
25. A (page 337)

CHAPTER 13

EDUCATION AND RELIGION

KEY TERMS

born again: a term describing Christians who have undergone a life-transforming religious experience so radical that they feel they have become a "new person"

charisma: an extraordinary gift from God; more commonly, an outstanding, "magnetic" personality

charismatic leader: literally, someone to whom God has given an extraordinary gift; more commonly, someone who exerts extraordinary appeal to a group of followers

church: to Durkheim, one of the three essential elements of religion—a moral community of believers; used by other sociologists to refer to a highly organized religious organization

cosmology: teachings or ideas that provide a unified picture of the world

credential society: a group that uses diplomas and degrees to determine who is eligible for jobs even though the diploma or degree may be irrelevant to the actual work

cult: a new religion with few followers, whose teachings are practices put it at odds with he dominant culture and religion

cultural transmission: in reference to education, the ways by which schools transmit culture, especially its core values

ecclesia: a religious group so integrated into the dominant culture that it is difficult to tell where the one begins and the other leaves off

functional illiterate: a high school graduate who has difficulty with basic reading and math

gatekeeping: the process by which education opens and closes doors of opportunity; another term for the social placement function of education

grade inflation: higher grades for the same work; a general rise in student grades without a corresponding increase in learning or test scores

hidden curriculum: the unwritten goals of schools, such as teaching obedience to authority and conformity to cultural norms

latent functions: unintended consequences of people's actions that help to keep a social system in equilibrium

mainstreaming: helping people to become part of the mainstream of society

manifest functions: intended consequences of people's actions designed to help some part of a social system

modernization: the process by which a *Gemeinschaft* society is transformed into a *Gesellschaft* society; the transformation of traditional societies into industrial societies

profane: Durkheim's term for common elements of everyday life

Protestant ethic: Weber's term to describe the ideal of a self-denying, moral life, accompanied by hard work and frugality

religion: to Emile Durkheim, beliefs and practices that separate the profane from the sacred and unite its adherents into a moral community

religious experience: awareness of the supernatural or a feeling of coming into contact with God

rituals: ceremonies or repetitive practices; in this context, religious observances or ties, often intended to evoke a sense of awe of the sacred

sacred: Durkheim's term for things set apart or forbidden, that inspire fear, awe, reverence, or deep respect

sect: a group larger than a cult that whose members feel hostility from and toward society

secularization of religion: the replacement of a religion's "otherworldly" concerns with concerns about "this world"

social placement: a function of education; funneling people into a society's various positions

social promotion: promoting students to the next grade even though they have not mastered basic materials

spirit of capitalism: Weber's term for the desire to accumulate capital as a duty—not to spend it, but as an end in itself—and to constantly reinvest it

tracking: sorting students into educational programs on the basis of real or perceived abilities

KEY PEOPLE

James Coleman and Thomas Hoffer: A study of students in Catholic and public high schools by these two sociologists demonstrated that performance was based on setting higher standards for students rather than on individual ability.

Randall Collins: Collins studied the credential society.

Kingsley Davis and Wilbert Moore: Davis and Moore argue that a major task of society is to fill social positions with capable people and that one of the functions of schools is gatekeeping—the funneling of people into these positions based on merit.

Emile Durkheim: Durkheim investigated world religions and identified elements that are common to all religions—separation of sacred from profane, beliefs about what is sacred, practices surrounded the sacred, and a moral community.

George Farkas: Farkas and a team of researchers investigated how teacher expectations affect student grades. They found that students signal teachers that they are good students by being eager, cooperative and working hard.

Benton Johnson: Johnson analyzed types of religious groups—cults, sects, churches, and ecclesia.

Karl Marx: Marx was critical of religion, calling it the opium of the masses.

Richard Niebuhr: This theologian suggested that the splintering of Christianity into numerous branches has more to do with social change than with religious conflict.

Talcott Parsons: Another functionalist who suggested that a function of schools is to funnel people into social positions.

Liston Pope: Another sociologist who studied types of religious groups.

Ray Rist: This sociologist's classic study of an African-American grade school uncovered some of the dynamics of educational tracking.

Thomas Sowell: Sowell has studied international differences in student performance.

Ernst Troeltsch: Yet another sociologist who is associated with types of reliigous groups from cults to ecclesia.

Max Weber: Weber studied the link between Protestantism and the rise of capitalism and found that the ethic associated with Protestant denominations was compatible with the needs of capitalism.

Essentials of Sociology
Sixth Edition

Chapter Thirteen: Education
and Religion

This multimedia product and its contents are protected under copyright law. The following are prohibited by law:
any public performance or display, including transmission of any image over a network;
preparation of any derivative work, including the extraction, in whole or in part, of any images;
any rental, lease, or lending of the program.

Chapter Overview

- Education in Global Perspective
- The Functionalist Perspective: Providing Social Benefits
- The Conflict Perspective: Reproducing the Social Class Structure
- The Symbolic Interactionist Perspective: Fulfilling Teacher Expectations
- Problems in United States Education and Their Solutions

- What is Religion?
- The Functionalist Perspective
- The Symbolic Interactionist Perspective
- The Conflict Perspective
- Religion and the Spirit of Capitalism
- Types of Religious Groups
- Religion in the United States
- The Future of Religion

Copyright © Allyn & Bacon 2006   2

Education in Global Perspective

❖ Credential Societies - Diplomas

  Determine Job Eligibility

❖ Diplomas Serve as Sorting Devices

❖ Education Related to Nation's Economy

Copyright © Allyn & Bacon 2006   3

Education in the Industrialized Nations

❖ Education in Japan

  ❖ Emphasis on Solidarity within Group

  ❖ Discourages Competition among Individuals

4

Education in the Industrializing Nations

❖ Education in Russia

  ❖ Education, including College was Free

  ❖ Post-Soviet Russians are "Reinventing" Education

5

Education in the Least Industrialized Nations

❖ Education in Egypt

  ❖ Mandatory Attendance Laws that Exist are Not Enforced

  ❖ Most People Work so Find Little Need for Education

  ❖ Most Cannot Afford Education

6

Functionalist Perspective
Providing Social Benefits

❖ Manifest vs. Latent Functions

❖ Teaching Knowledge and Skills

❖ Cultural Transmission of Values

❖ Social Integration

❖ Gatekeeping

Copyright © Allyn & Bacon 2006

Conflict Perspective
Perpetuating Social Inequality

❖ The Hidden Curriculum

❖ Tilting the Tests: Discrimination by IQ

❖ Stacking the Deck: Unequal Funding

Copyright © Allyn & Bacon 2006   8

Symbolic Interactionist Perspective
Fulfilling Teacher Expectations

❖ The Rist Research

❖ George Farkas and Teacher Expectations

❖ How Do Teacher Expectations Work?

Copyright © Allyn & Bacon 2006   9

Problems in U.S. Education

❖ Rising Tide of Mediocrity

❖ Cheating on SATs

❖ Grade Inflation, Social Promotion,

Functional Illiteracy

❖ The Influence of Peer Groups

❖ Violence in Schools

10

Solutions: Safety and Standards

❖ Secure Learning Environment

❖ Higher Standards

11

What is Religion?

Emile Durkheim said, "A religion is a

unified system of beliefs and practices

relative to sacred things."

12

Three Elements of Religion

❖ *Beliefs* that Some Things are Sacred

❖ *Practices* Centering on Things Considered Sacred

❖ A *Moral Community* Resulting from a Group's Beliefs and Practices

13

The Functionalist Perspective
Functions of Religion

❖ Questions about Ultimate Meaning

❖ Social Solidarity

❖ Emotional Comfort

❖ Guidelines for Everyday Life

❖ Sometimes Spearheads Change

14

The Functionalist Perspective
Dysfunctions of Religion

❖ Religious Persecution

❖ War and Terrorism

15

Symbolic Interactionist Perspective

* ❖ Religious Symbols
* ❖ Rituals, Ceremonies, Repetitive Practices
* ❖ Beliefs - Cosmology
* ❖ Religious Experience - Contact with God
* ❖ Born Again

Copyright © Allyn & Bacon 2006

Conflict Perspective

* ❖ Marx's Opium of the People
* ❖ Legitimization of Social Inequalities
  * ❖ Social Arrangements Represent God's Desires
  * ❖ Divine Rights of Kings
  * ❖ Pharaoh as God
  * ❖ Hindu Cast System

Copyright © Allyn & Bacon 2006   17

Religion and the Spirit of Capitalism

* ❖ Weber - Religion Held the Key to Modernization
* ❖ Protestant Ethic
  * ❖ Personal Duty to Make and Invest Money
  * ❖ A Move away from Traditional Thrift
  * ❖ Good Works Show Salvation
  * ❖ Lead Moral Lives and Work Hard
  * ❖ Spend Only on Necessities, Reinvest the Rest
  * ❖ Change from Catholicism to Protestantism

Copyright © Allyn & Bacon 2006   18

Types of Religious Groups

❖ **Cults**
  ❖ Begin with Charismatic Leader
  ❖ Most Popular Religions Started this Way
  ❖ Most Cults Fail

❖ **Sects**
  ❖ Loosely Organized and Fairly Small
  ❖ Emphasize Personal Salvation

Copyright © Allyn & Bacon 2006   19

Types of Religious Groups

❖ **Churches**
  ❖ Highly Bureaucratized
  ❖ National and International
  ❖ Relationship with God Less Intense

❖ **Ecclesia**
  ❖ State Religions
  ❖ Part of Cultural Identification

Copyright © Allyn & Bacon 2006   20

Religion in the U.S.

❖ Characteristics of Members

  ❖ Social Class

  ❖ Race and Ethnicity

  ❖ Age

Copyright © Allyn & Bacon 2006   21

Religion in the U.S.

❖ Characteristics of Religious Groups

   ❖Diversity

   ❖Pluralism and Freedom

   ❖Competition and Recruitment

Copyright © Allyn & Bacon 2006   22

Religion in the U.S.

❖ Characteristics of Religious Groups

   ❖Fundamentalist Revival

   ❖The Electronic Church

Copyright © Allyn & Bacon 2006   23

Secularization and Splintering of U.S. Churches

❖ Disagreements about Doctrine

❖ Social Change

❖ The Secularization of Religion

Copyright © Allyn & Bacon 2006   24

The Future of Religion

❖ Religion Thrives

❖ People will Always Ponder Purpose

❖ Science Cannot Tell Us About…

  ❖ The Existence of God

  ❖ The Purpose of Life

  ❖ An Afterlife

  ❖ Morality

25

Essentials of Sociology

Sixth Edition

Chapter Thirteen: Education
and Religion

This multimedia product and its contents are protected under copyright law. The following are prohibited by law: any public performance or display, including transmission of any image over a network; preparation of any derivative work, including the extraction, in whole or in part, of any images; any rental, lease, or lending of the program.

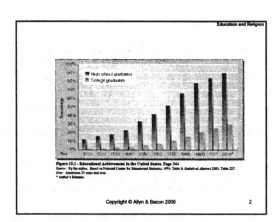

Figure 13.1 - Educational Achievement in the United States. Page 344
Source: By the author. Based on National Center for Educational Statistics, 1991: Table 8; *Statistical Abstract* 2003: Table 227.
Note: Americans 25 years and over.
* Author's Estimate.

2

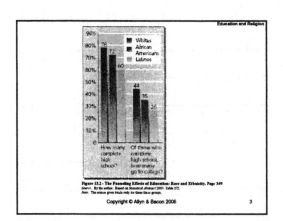

Figure 13.2 - The Funneling Effects of Education: Race and Ethnicity. Page 349
Source: By the author. Based on *Statistical Abstract* 2003: Table 272.
Note: The census gives totals only for these three groups.

3

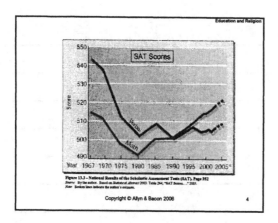

Figure 13.3 - National Results of the Scholastic Assessment Tests (SAT). Page 352
Source: By the author. Based on *Statistical Abstract* 2003: Table 264; "SAT Scores..." 2003.
Note: Broken lines indicate the author's estimate.

4

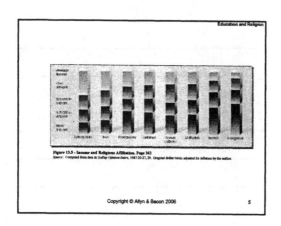

Figure 13.5 - Income and Religious Affiliation. Page 363
Source: Compiled from data in *Gallup Opinion Index,* 1987:20-27, 29. Original dollar totals adjusted for inflation by the author.

5

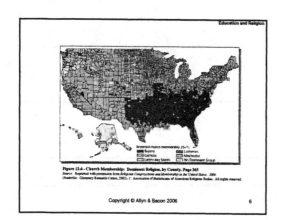

Figure 13.6 - Church Membership: Dominant Religion, by County. Page 365
Source: Reprinted with permission from *Religious Congregations and Membership in the United States: 2000*
(Nashville: Glenmary Research Center, 2002). C. Association of Statisticians of American Religious Bodies. All rights reserved.

6

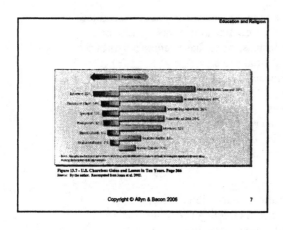

Figure 13.7 - U.S. Churches: Gains and Losses in Ten Years. Page 366
Source: By the author. Reconstructed from Jones et al. 2002.

7

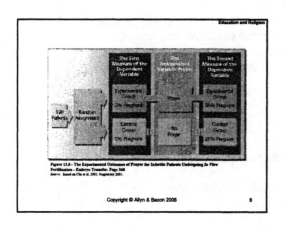

Figure 13.8 - The Experimental Outcomes of Prayer for Infertile Patients Undergoing *In Vitro*
Fertilization - Embryo Transfer. Page 368
Source: Based on Cha et al. 2001; Nagourney 2001.

8

1. The Acme Company recently rewrote all of its personnel requirements. For menial, unskilled positions a high school diploma or GED is required. For career track positions a bachelor's degree (in any discipline) is required. Based on these changes, Acme has become a part of the:
   a. meritocracy
   b. gerontocracy
   c. credential society
   d. bureaucracy

2. Sociologist Randall Collins defined *credential society* as
   a. a society that uses degrees and diplomas to determine who gets jobs.
   b. a society that has established formal means of passing on cultural values.
   c. a society that relies on informal means of passing on culture.
   d. a society that uses only accredited school boards.

3. A central sociological principle of education is that a nation's education reflects:
   a. that nation's gross national product
   b. that nation's culture
   c. the natural intelligence of its citizens
   d. that nation's type of government

4. In Japan, how do high school seniors find a college to attend?
   a. There is a college available to anyone with the desire to attend and the money to afford it.
   b. College placement is primarily for the wealthy who attend expensive prep schools.
   c. There are so many qualified seniors and so few colleges that admission is by lottery.
   d. Only the top scorers on the national test, regardless of income, are admitted to college.

5. Education's most manifest function is to:
   a. provide child care
   b. transmit values
   c. teach knowledge and skills
   d. bring about social integration

6. A process by which schools pass a society's core values from one generation to the next is referred to as:
   a. the hidden curriculum
   b. cultural transmission
   c. the track and level system
   d. gatekeeping

7. Molding students into a more cohesive unit by holding exercises such as saluting the flag and singing the national anthem brings about:
   a. social integration
   b. social solidarity
   c. manifest destiny
   d. cultural identity

8. When schools incorporate students with disabilities into regular social activities it referred to as:
   a. gatekeeping
   b. tracking
   c. social placement
   d. mainstreaming

9. When Leo, Matthew, and Ryan entered high school Leo was placed in an honors program, Matthew in the college prep courses, and Ryan in the general curriculum where he takes vocational courses. These placements were made after reviewing test scores and teacher recommendations. Such placements are referred to as:
   a. cultural transmission
   b. credentialing
   c. tracking
   d. social promotion

10. Talcott Parsons, Kingsley Davis, and Wilbert Moore pioneered a view known as
    _____ arguing that some jobs require few skills and can be performed by people of
    less intellectual capability while others require only the most gifted and studious.
    a. credentialing   c. mainstreaming
    b. social placement   d. the hidden curriculum

11. Sociologist Ray Rist conducted research that demonstrated:
    a. the difference in ability among students of different racial backgrounds.
    b. the cultural bias that exists in standardized tests.
    c. the need to desegregate schools.
    d. the impact of a student being labeled by teachers in respect to their success.

12. George Farkas discovered that some students with the same test scores actually get better grades
    because:
    a. some schools are racially insensitive and discriminate based on color.
    b. some students "signal" their teachers they are good students.
    c. some students took easier exams and others took more difficult exams.
    d. teachers use the bell shaped curve which requires different grades to be awarded.

13. The practice of passing students from one grade to the next even though they have not mastered
    the basic material is called:
    a. grade inflation   c. social promotion
    b. functional illiteracy   d. tracking

14. People who are united by their religious practices are referred to as being a/an:
    a. moral community   c. theology
    b. ecclesia   d. sacred assembly

15. Which of the following is *not* a dysfunction of religion?
    a. War   c. Religious persecution
    b. Terrorism   d. Providing answers to perplexing questions

16. A general conclusion about the role of ritual in religion is that rituals
    a. involve ceremonies that are unique, non-repetitive practices.
    b. do not include everyday practices such as singing in a church.
    c. are found in Christian churches but not those of other religions.
    d. can serve as a means of uniting people into a moral community.

17. Ceremonies or repetitive practices that help unite people into a moral community are referred to as:
    a. a religious experience   c. rituals
    b. services   d. cosmology

18. Jews, Christians, and Muslims have a unified picture of the world that includes the belief in one
    God. This unified picture is referred to as:
    a. ritualism   c. ecumenical beliefs
    b. holy communion   d. cosmology

19. "Religion is the opium of the people" was a term used by _____ to demonstrate
    that oppressed workers escape into religion.
    a. Emile Durkheim   c. Max Weber
    b. Karl Marx   d. Joseph Stalin

20. Max Weber believed religion held the key to the transformation of traditional societies into industrial studies, a process known as _____.
    a. modernization
    b. bureaucratization
    c. capitalism
    d. positivism

21. What was Weber's view on the function of religion?
    a. Religion is the key to modernization of capitalist industrial societies.
    b. Religion prevents the working class from realizing their exploitation.
    c. Religion unites like-minded people in a moral community.
    d. Religion is an expression of society's basic morality.

22. The term "new religion" is a more neutral and politically correct description of the type of religious group called a/an:
    a. sect   b. church   c. ecclesia   d. cult

23. A charismatic leader is most likely going to be the head of a/an:
    a. ecclesia   b. church   c. moral community   d. cult

24. What is an ecclesia?
    a. a religious group that is thoroughly integrated into the dominant culture
    b. a religious group that has substantial differences with the dominant culture
    c. a small religious group rejected and often persecuted by the dominant culture
    d. a small religious group accepted by the dominant culture

25. Which of the following questions can science answer?
    a. Does God exist?
    b. Is there an afterlife?
    c. What is the purpose of life?
    d. How does a cause relate to an effect?

PRACTICE TEST — ANSWER KEY

1. C (page 342)
2. A (page 342)
3. B (page 342)
4. D (pages 343-344)
5. C (page 346)
6. B (page 346)
7. A (page 346)
8. D (page 347)
9. C (page 348)

10. B (page 348)
11. D (pages 350-351)
12. B (page 351)
13. C (page 352)
14. A (page 356)
15. D (page 356)
16. D (page 358)
17. C (page 358)
18. D (page 359)

19. B (page 359)
20. A (page 360)
21. C (page 360)
22. D (page 361)
23. B (page 361)
24. A (page 362)
25. D (page 367)

CHAPTER 14

POPULATION AND URBANIZATION

KEY TERMS

alienation: a sense of not belonging, and a feeling that no one cares what happens to you

basic demographic equation: growth rate = births – deaths + net migration

city: a place in which a large number of people are permanently based and do not produce their own food

community: a place people identify with, where they sense that they belong and that others care what happens to them

crude birth rate: the annual number of births per 1,000 population

crude death rate: the annual number of deaths per 1,000 population

deindustrialization: a process by which fewer people work in manufacturing; one reason is automation, while another is the globalization of capitalism, which moves manufacturing jobs to countries where labor costs are less

demographic transition: a three-stage historical process of population growth; first, high birth rates and high death rates; second, high birth rates and low death rates; and third, low birth rates and low death rates; a fourth stage of population shrinkage may be emerging

demographic variables: the three factors that influence population growth: fertility, mortality, and net migration

demography: the study of the size, composition, growth, and distribution of human populations

disinvestment: the withdrawal of investments by banks, which seals the fate of an urban area

edge city: a large clustering of service facilities and residences near a highway intersection that provides a sense of place to people who live, shop, and work there

enterprise zone: the use of economic incentives in a designated area with the intention of encouraging investment there

exponential growth curve: a pattern of growth in which numbers double during approximately equal intervals, thus accelerating in the latter stages

fertility rate: the number of children that the average woman bears

gentrification: the displacement of the poor as the relatively affluent purchase and renovate their homes

growth rate: the net change in a population after adding births, subtracting deaths, and either adding or subtracting net migration

human ecology: Robert Park's term for the relationship between people and their environment (natural resources such as land); also called *human ecology*

invasion-succession cycle: the process of one group of people displacing a group whose racial-ethnic or social class characteristics differ from their own

Malthus theorem: an observation by Thomas Malthus that although the food supply increases arithmetically, population grows geometrically

megalopolis: an urban area consisting of at least two metropolises and their many suburbs

metropolis: a central city surrounded by smaller cities and their suburbs

metropolitan statistical area (MSA): a central city and the urbanized counties adjacent to it

net migration rate: the difference between the number of immigrants and emigrants per 1,000 population

population pyramid: a graphic representation of a population, divided into age and sex

population shrinkage: the process by which a country's population becomes smaller because its birth rate and immigration are too low to replace those who die and emigrate

redlining: the officers of a bank refusing to make loans in a particular area

suburb: a community adjacent to a city

suburbanization: the movement from the city to the suburbs

urbanization: an increasing proportion of a population living in cities and those cities having a growing influence in their society

urban renewal: the rehabilitation of a rundown area of a city, which usually results in the displacement of the poor who are living in that area

zero population growth: a demographic condition in which woman bear only enough children to reproduce the population

KEY PEOPLE

Ernest Burgess: Burgess developed the concentric zone model of urban development.

John Darley and Bibb Latane: these social psychologists uncovered a *diffusion of responsibility*—the more bystanders there are to an incident, the less likely anyone is to help.

William Flanagan: Flanagan has suggested three guiding principles for finding solutions to pressing urban problems—use of regional planning, awareness of human needs, and equalizing the benefits as well as the impact of urban change.

Herbert Gans: Gans studied urban neighborhoods, with the result that he documented the existence of community within cities and identified the several types of urban dwellers that live there.

Chauncey Harris and Edward Ullman: These two geographers developed the multiple-nuclei model of urban growth.

Homer Hoyt: Hoyt modified Burgess's model of urban development with his sector model.

Donald Huddle: this economist uses figures to show that immigrants are a drain on taxpayers.

David Karp and William Yoels: These sociologists note that identification with a city's sports teams can be so intense that even after an individual moves away from the city, he continues to root for the team.

Thomas Malthus: Malthus was an economist who made dire predictions about the future of population growth.

Robert Park: Park coined the term "human ecology" to describe how people adapt to their environment.

Julian Simon: Simon is an anti-Malthusian who believes people do not just reproduce blindly but act intelligently and plan rationally. Simon has also argued that immigrants are a net contributor on the U.S. economy.

Louis Wirth: Wirth wrote a classic essay, "Urbanism as a Way of Life," in which he argued that city life undermines kinship and neighborhood.

Essentials of Sociology
Sixth Edition

Chapter Fourteen: Population and Urbanization

Chapter Overview

❖ A Planet with No Space to Enjoy Life?

❖ Population Growth

❖ The Development of Cities—Urbanization

❖ City Life: Alienation and Community

❖ Urban Problems and Social Policy

2

Population in Global Perspective

❖No Space for Enjoying Life?

❖The New Malthusians

❖The Anti-Malthusians

❖Who is Correct?

3

Population in Global Perspective

❖ Why Are People

Starving?

   ❖ Now More Food Per Person

   Produced

   ❖ Starvation Occurs in Particular

   Places

     ❖ Droughts

     ❖ Wars   Copyright © Allyn & Bacon 2006

Population Growth

❖ Why Do Least Industrialized Nations

Have So Many Children?

  ❖ Status of Parenthood

  ❖ Community Support

  ❖ Reliance on Children in Old Age

Copyright © Allyn & Bacon 2006   5

Population Growth

❖ Implications of Different Growth Rates

  ❖ Population Pyramids

  ❖ Population Momentum

  ❖ Standards of Living

Copyright © Allyn & Bacon 2006   6

Population Growth

❖ Demographic Variables

  ❖ Fertility

  ❖ Mortality

  ❖ Migration

7

Population Growth

❖ Problems in Forecasting Population Growth

  ❖ Basic Demographic Equation

  ❖ Growth Rate=Births - Deaths + Net Migration

❖ Countries that Industrialize have Birth Rate Declines

❖ Zero Population Growth

8

Urbanization

❖ The Development of Cities

❖ The Process of Urbanization

  ❖ Metropolises

  ❖ Megalopolises

9

Urbanization

❖U.S. Urban Patterns

   ❖From Country to City

   ❖From City to City

   ❖Between Cities

   ❖Within the City

   ❖From City to Country Suburbanization

10

Models of Urban Growth

❖The Concentric Zone Model

❖The Sector Model

❖The Multiple-Nuclei Model

❖The Peripheral Model

11

Models of Urban Growth

❖ Critique of the Models

   ❖ They are Time Bound

   ❖ They Do Not Account for Urban Planning

   ❖ Fall Short with Cities in Least Industrialized

     Nations

12

City Life

❖Community - A Feeling that We Belong

❖Alienation - A Sense of Not Belonging

❖Who Lives in the City?
- ❖The Cosmopolites
- ❖The Singles
- ❖The Ethnic Villagers
- ❖The Deprived
- ❖The Trapped

Copyright © Allyn & Bacon 2006   13

City Life

❖ Urban Sentiment: Finding a Familiar

World

- ❖ City Divided into Little Worlds
- ❖ People Create Intimacy by Personalizing Shopping
- ❖ Spectator Sports Provide Venue

Copyright © Allyn & Bacon 2006   14

City Life

❖Norm of Noninvolvement

❖Diffusion of Responsibility

❖The Rural Rebound

Copyright © Allyn & Bacon 2006   15

Urban Problems and Social Policy

❖ Suburbanization

   ❖ Movement of People from Cities to Suburbs Located Outside Cities

   ❖ City Centers Lose in Transition

   16

Urban Problems and Social Policy

❖City Versus Suburb

❖Suburban Flight

❖Disinvestment and Deindustrialization

❖Potential Urban Revitalization

   17

Urban Problems and Social Policy

❖Potential Urban Revitalization

   ❖Urban Renewal

   ❖Enterprise Zones

   ❖Building Community

     ❖ Scale

     ❖ Livability

     ❖ Social Justice

   18

Essentials of Sociology

Sixth Edition

Chapter Fourteen: Population and Urbanization

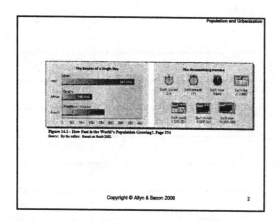

Figure 14.1 - How Fast is the World's Population Growing?. Page 374
Source: By the author. Based on Haub 2002.

2

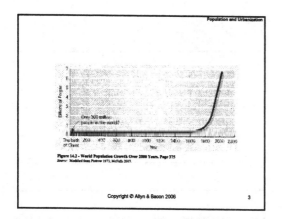

Figure 14.2 - World Population Growth Over 2000 Years. Page 375
Source: Modified from Piotrow 1973, McFalls 2003.

3

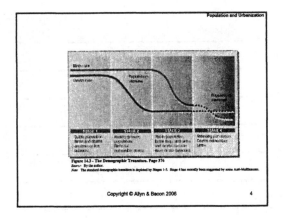

Figure 14.3 - The Demographic Transition. Page 376
Source: By the author.
Note The standard demographic transition is depicted by Stages 1-3. Stage 4 has recently been suggested by some Anti-Malthusians.

4

___

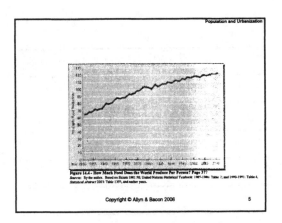

Figure 14.4 - How Much Food Does the World Produce Per Person? Page 377
Sources: By the author. Based on Simon 1981:56; United Nations *Statistical Yearbook* 1985-1986: Table 7; and 1990-1991: Table 4, *Statistical Abstract* 2003: Table 1355, and earlier years.

5

___

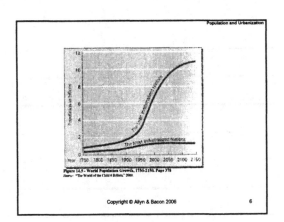

Figure 14.5 - World Population Growth, 1750-2150. Page 378
Source: "The World of the Child 6 Billion," 2000.

6

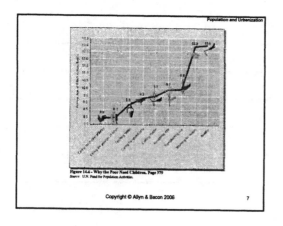

Figure 14.6 - Why the Poor Need Children, Page 379
Source: U.N. Fund for Population Activities.

7

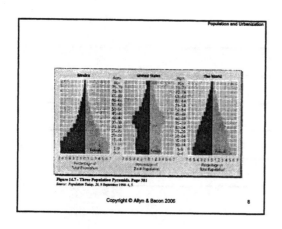

Figure 14.7 - Three Population Pyramids, Page 381
Source: Population Today, 26, 9 September 1998: 4, 5.

8

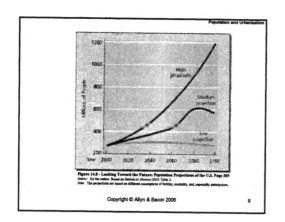

Figure 14.8 - Looking Toward the Future: Population Projections of the U.S. Page 385
Source: By the author. Based on *Statistical Abstract* 2003: Table 3.
Note: The projections are based on different assumptions of fertility, mortality, and, especially, immigration.

9

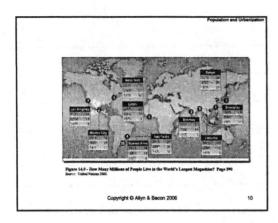

Figure 14.9 - How Many Millions of People Live in the World's Largest Megacities? Page 390
Source: United Nations 2000.

10

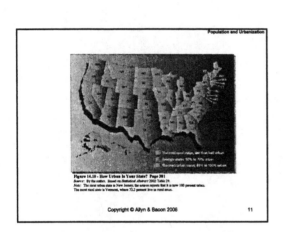

Figure 14.10 - How Urban Is Your State? Page 391
Source: By the author. Based on *Statistical Abstract* 2002:Table 29.
Note: The most urban state is New Jersey; the source reports that it is now 100 percent urban.
The most rural state is Vermont, where 72.2 percent live in rural areas.

11

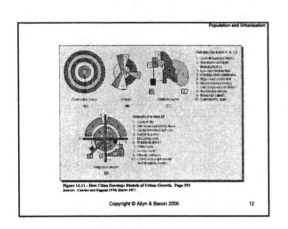

Figure 14.11 - How Cities Develop: Models of Urban Growth. Page 393
Sources: Cousins and Nagpaul 1970; Harris 1997.

12

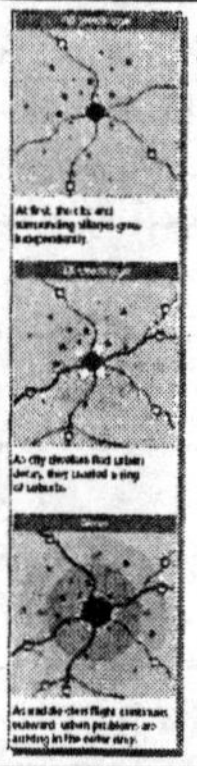

Figure 14.12 - Urban
Growth and Urban Flight.
Page 400

At first, the city and
surrounding villages grew
independently.

As city elevators that urban
area, they pushed a ring
of suburbs.

As urban-then-flight continues,
suburbs' urban problems are
pushing to the outer area.

13

PRACTICE TEST

1. The study of the size, composition, growth, and distribution of human populations is called:
   a. geography   b. demography   c. political science   d. anthropology

2. Thomas Malthus predicted worldwide starvation because population increases _____ while food supply can only increase _____.
   a. geometrically/arithmetically
   b. metaphysically/mathematically
   c. geologically/agriculturally
   d. astrologically/geographically

3. The "Anti-Mathusians" rely on which of the following theories to explain changing population growth patterns?
   a. Dependency Theory
   b. Demographic Transition Theory
   c. World Systems Theory
   d. Social Disengagement Theory

4. The demographic transition is correctly illustrated by which of the following descriptions?
   a. Stage one has high birthrates and low death rates.
   b. Stage two has low birthrates and high death rates.
   c. Stage one has low birthrates and high death rates.
   d. Stage two has high birthrates and low death rates.

5. Corinne is studying the population of Europe and is viewing graph-like grids resembling a triangle that show a country's population by age and sex. Corinne is using a/an:
   a. population parallelogram
   b. genealogical chart
   c. population pyramid
   d. basic demographic equation

6. The three demographic variables that comprise the basic demographic equation are:
   a. population, economics, and geography
   b. income, politics, and social class
   c. age, race, and class
   d. fertility, mortality, and migration

7. The net migration rate is arrived at by:
   a. subtracting the number of emigrants from immigrants per 1000
   b. adding the number of emigrants and the number of immigrants per 1000
   c. multiplying the number of immigrants by the emigrants and dividing by 1000
   d. dividing the number of immigrants by the number of emigrants and multiplying by 1000

8. People who move into a country are referred to as _____; whereas people who move out of a country are referred to as _____.
   a. emigrants/immigrants
   b. immigrants/emigrants
   c. migrants/movers
   d. relocators/migrants

9. The nation that is the world's number one choice for immigration is:
   a. Australia
   b. The United States
   c. Canada
   d. Great Britain

10. Examples of push factors include all of the following *except*:
   a. Poverty
   b. Persecution for religious ideas
   c. Persecution for political ideas
   d. Higher wages

11. To achieve zero population growth, every 1,000 women would need to give birth to how many children?
    a. 1,000　　　　　 b. 1,200　　　　　 c. 2,000　　　　　 d. 2,100

12. Around 3,500 BC the first cities appeared:
    a. along the Nile River
    b. in Mesopotamia
    c. along the Yellow River
    d. in West Africa

13. By what year did half of Americans live in cities?
    a. 1840　　　　　 b. 1900　　　　　 c. 1920　　　　　 d. 1942

14. Masses of people moving to cities with these cities having a growing influence on society is referred to as:
    a. urbanization
    b. suburbanization
    c. gentrification
    d. modernization

15. The movement of middle class people into run down areas of a city where they renovate and improve the quality of the homes they purchase is referred to as:
    a. succession　　　 b. gentrification　　　 c. urbanization　　　 d. suburbanization

16. Which two states have a "fastest growing city"?
    a. New York and Pennsylvania
    b. Ohio and Massachusetts
    c. New York and Nevada
    d. Arizona and Utah

17. The negative consequence of gentrification is:
    a. an improvement in the appearance of some urban neighborhoods.
    b. poor residents are displaced by the more well-to-do newcomers.
    c. buildings are freshly painted and lawns are freshly groomed.
    d. middle class families moving into poorly constructed buildings.

18. The term human ecology, which is used to describe how people adapt to their environment, was coined by sociologist _____.
    a. Richard Cloward
    b. Talcott Parsons
    c. Herbert Spencer
    d. Robert Park

19. In the Concentric Zone Model, the zone of the city that is in transition that breeds poverty, disease, and vice is:
    a. Zone I　　　 b. Zone II　　　 c. Zone III　　　 d. Zone IV

20. A sense of not belonging and a feeling that no one cares that city dwellers are prone to experience is called:
    a. Alienation　　　 b. Compurgation　　　 c. Urbanization　　　 d. Modernization

21. The type of city dweller that includes students, intellectuals, professionals, musicians, artists, and entertainers is the:
    a. Cosmopolites　　　 b. Singles　　　 c. Ethnic Villagers　　　 d. Trapped

22. Which category of people is least likely to live in an American city by choice?
    a. cosmopolites
    b. the deprived
    c. single people
    d. ethnic villagers

23. The "norm of noninvolvement" that pertains to many urban dwellers refers to:
    a. many city dwellers avoiding intrusion from strangers and "tuning others out".
    b. the number of city dwellers who are unemployed or on welfare.
    c. apathy among city dwellers that results in low voting turnout.
    d. the low number of eligible city dwellers who attend local college and cultural events.

24. Which of the following is a "push" factor for individuals and families moving to rural communities?
    a. fear of urban crime and violence
    b. safety
    c. lower cost of living
    d. recreation and more space

25. The withdrawal of investment income to create businesses or to purchase housing in a problem area of a city is referred to as:
    a. deindustrialization
    b. disinvestment
    c. suburban flight
    d. gentrification

PRACTICE TEST — ANSWER KEY

1. B (page 374)
2. A (page 374)
3. B (page 375)
4. D (page 376)
5. C (page 380-381)
6. D (page 381-382)
7. A (page 382)
8. B (page 382)
9. B (page 382)

10. D (page 382)
11. D (page 385)
12. B (page 386)
13. C (page 387)
14. A (page 387)
15. B (page 390)
16. D (page 390-391)
17. B (page 390)
18. D (page 392)

19. B (page 392)
20. A (page 394)
21. A (page 396)
22. B (page 396)
23. A (page 397)
24. A (page 397)
25. B (page 400)

CHAPTER 15

SOCIAL CHANGE:
TECHNOLOGY, SOCIAL MOVEMENTS AND THE ENVIRONMENT

KEY TERMS

acid rain: rain containing sulfuric and nitric acid; the result of burning fossil fuels

alterative social movement: a social movement that seeks to alter only particular aspects of people

corporate welfare: benefits (such as tax breaks or stadiums) given corporations to locate or to remain in an area

cultural lag: William Ogburn's term for human behavior lagging behind technological innovation

dialectical process: a view of history and power in which each arrangement, or thesis, contains contradictions, or antitheses, which must be resolved; the new arrangement, or synthesis, contains its own contradictions, and so on

diffusion: the spread of invention and discovery from one area to another; identified by William Ogburn as a major process of social change

discovery: a new way of seeing reality; identified by William Ogburn as a major process of social change

ecosabotage: actions taken to sabotage the efforts of people thought to be legally harming the environment

environmental racism: the greater impact of pollution on the poor and racial minorities

environmental sociology: a subdiscipline of sociology that examines how human activities affect the physical environment and how the physical environment affects human activities

global warming: an increase in the earth's temperature due to the greenhouse effect

greenhouse effect: the buildup of carbon dioxide in the earth's atmosphere that allows light to enter but inhibits the release of heat; believed to cause global warming

invention: the combination of existing elements and materials to form new ones; identified by William Ogburn as a major process of social change

modernization: the transformation of traditional societies into industrial societies

postmodern society: another term for postindustrial society

proactive social movement: a social movement that promotes social change

propaganda: in its broad sense, the presentation of information in the attempt to influence people; in its narrow sense, one-sided information used to try to influence people

public opinion: how people think about some issue

reactive social movement: a social movement that resists social change

redemptive social movement: a social movement that seeks to change people totally

reformative social movement: a social movement that seeks to reform some specific aspect of society

resource mobilization: a stage that social movements succeed or fail based on their ability to mobilize resources such as time, money, and people's skills

social change: the alteration of culture and societies over time

social movement: large numbers of people who organize to promote or resist social change

social movement organization: an organization developed to further the goals of a social movement

sustainable environment: a world system in which we use our physical environment to meet the needs of humanity and leave a heritage of a sound environment to the next generation

technology: often defined as the applications of science, but can be thought of as tools, items used to accomplish tasks, along with the skills or procedures to make and use those tools

transformative social movement: a social movement that seeks to change society totally

KEY PEOPLE

David Aberle: Arbele classified social movements into four types: alterative, redemptive, reformative, and transformation based on the amount of intended change and the target of the change.

Alfred & Elizabeth Lee: These sociologists found that propaganda relies on seven basic techniques, which they labeled "tricks of the trade."

Karl Marx: Marx analyzed the emergence of capitalism and developed the theory of dialectical materialism.

John McCarthy and Mayer Zald: These sociologists investigated the resource mobilization of social movements and found that, although there may be a group of angry and agitated people, without this mobilization they will never become a social movement.

Lewis Henry Morgan: Morgan's theory of social development once dominated Western thought. He suggested that societies pass through three stages: savagery, barbarism, and civilization.

William Ogburn: Ogburn identified three processes of social change: invention, discovery, and diffusion. He also coined the term "cultural lag" to describe a situation in which some elements of culture adapt to an invention or discovery more rapidly than others.

Oswald Spengler: Spengler wrote *The Decline of the West* in which he proposed that Western civilization was declining.

Arnold Toynbee: This historian suggests that each time a civilization successfully meets a challenge, oppositional forces are set up. Eventually, the oppositional forces are set loose, and the fabric of society is ripped apart.

Max Weber: Weber argued that capitalism grew out of the Protestant Reformation.

Mayer Zald: In analyzing social movements, Zald suggested that they were like a rolling sea, hitting society like a wave.

Essentials of Sociology

Sixth Edition

Chapter Fifteen: Social Change:
Technology, Social Movements,
and the Environment

This multimedia product and its contents are protected under copyright law. The following are prohibited by law: any public performance or display, including transmission of any image over a network; preparation of any derivative work, including the extraction, in whole or in part, of any images; any rental, lease, or lending of the program.

Chapter Overview

❖ How Social Change
Transforms Social
Life

❖ Theories and
Processes of Social
Change

❖ How Technology
Changes Society

❖ Social Movements as
a Source of Social
Change

❖ The Growth Machine
versus the Earth

Copyright © Allyn & Bacon 2006   2

How Social Change Transforms Social Life

❖ Four Social Revolutions

❖ From *Gemeinschaft* to *Gesellschaft*

❖ Capitalism, Modernization, and

  Industrialization

❖ Conflict, Power, and Global Politics

Copyright © Allyn & Bacon 2006   3

Theories and Processes of Social Change

❖ Cultural Evolution

❖ Natural Cycles

❖ Conflict Over Power

Copyright © Allyn & Bacon 2006

Theories and Processes of Social Change

❖ Ogburn's Theory

  ❖ Invention

  ❖ Discovery

  ❖ Diffusion

  ❖ Cultural Lag

Copyright © Allyn & Bacon 2006   5

How Technology Changes Society

❖ Technology is Tools and Skills

❖ Postmodern Societies Possess

   Technology that Greatly Extend Human

   Ability

Copyright © Allyn & Bacon 2006   6

The Cutting Edge of Change

❖ Computers in Education

❖ Computers in Medicine

❖ Computers in Business and Finance

❖ Changes in the War on Terrorism

Copyright © Allyn & Bacon 2006   7

Cyberspace and Social Inequality

❖ Access to Libraries of Information

❖ World Linked by Almost

   Instantaneous Communication

❖ National and Global Stratification

   Represents a Digital Divide

Copyright © Allyn & Bacon 2006   8

Social Movements as a Source of Social Change

❖ Social Movements - People Organizing

   to Promote or Resist Social Change

❖ Proactive Social Movements

❖ Reactive Social Movements

❖ Social Movement Organizations

Copyright © Allyn & Bacon 2006   9

Social Change: Technology, Social Movements, and the Environment

Social Movements as a Source of Social Change
Types of Social Movements

❖ Alternative Social Movements

❖ Redemptive Social Movements

❖ Reformative Social Movements

10

Social Change: Technology, Social Movements, and the Environment

Social Movements as a Source of Social Change
Types of Social Movements

❖ Transformative Social Movements

❖ Transnational Social Movements

❖ Metaformative Social Movements

11

Social Change: Technology, Social Movements, and the Environment

Propaganda and the Mass Media

❖ **Propaganda** - Presentation of Information that Distorts Reality

❖ Attempts to Influence Public Opinion

❖ Sociology Sensitized us to Multiple Realities

12

Stages of Social Movements

❖ Initial Unrest and Agitation

❖ Resource Mobilization

❖ Organization

❖ Institutionalization

❖ Organizational Decline or Resurgence

Copyright © Allyn & Bacon 2006   13

The Growth Machine vs. The Earth

❖ Environmental Problems in the

Most Industrialized Nations

   ❖ Industrial Growth at the Cost of Natural Environment

   ❖ Major Polluters in Most Industrialized Nations

Copyright © Allyn & Bacon 2006   14

The Growth Machine vs. The Earth

❖ Fossil Fuels and the

Environment

❖ The Energy Shortage and

Multinational Corporations

❖ Environmental Injustice

Copyright © Allyn & Bacon 2006   15

Environmental Problems in Industrializing Nations

❖ Ozone Depletion

❖ Greenhouse Effect

❖ Global Warming

Copyright © Allyn & Bacon 2006

16

Environmental Problems in Industrializing Nations

❖ Exported Pollution from

   Industrialized Nations

❖ Destruction of Habitat

❖ Disappearance of Rain Forests

Copyright © Allyn & Bacon 2006

17

Environmental Movement

❖ Rise of Green Parties

❖ Activists Seek Solutions in Politics,

   Education, and Legislation

❖ Ecosabotage

Copyright © Allyn & Bacon 2006

18

Environmental Sociology

❖ Main Assumptions:

❖ Physical Environment a Variable in Sociological Investigation

❖ Humans One Species Among Many

❖ Human Actions have Unintended Consequences

❖ The World is Finite

Copyright © Allyn & Bacon 2006   19

_____

_____

_____

_____

_____

_____

Environmental Sociology

❖ Main Assumptions:

❖ Economic Expansion Requires Increased Extraction of Resources

❖ Increased Extraction Leads to Ecological Problems

❖ Ecological Problems Restrict Economic Expansion

❖ Governments Create Environmental Problems

Copyright © Allyn & Bacon 2006   20

_____

_____

_____

_____

_____

_____

Environmental Sociology

❖ Technology and the Environment: The Goal of Harmony

❖ Abuse of Environment Not Inevitable

❖ Must Discover Ways to Reduce or Eliminate Harm to the Environment

Copyright © Allyn & Bacon 2006   21

_____

_____

_____

_____

_____

_____

Essentials of Sociology

Sixth Edition

Chapter Fifteen: Social Change -
Technology, Social Movements,
and the Environment

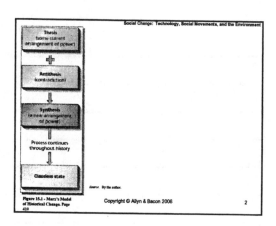

Figure 15.1 - Marx's Model of Historical Change. Page 410

Source: By the author.

2

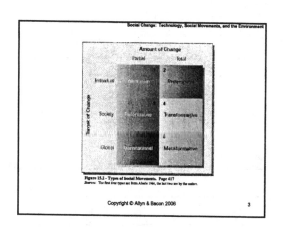

Figure 15.2 - Types of Social Movements. Page 417
Sources: The first four types are from Aberle 1966, the last two are by the author.

3

Figure 15.3 - How Does Your State Rank? Location of the Worst Industrial Waste Sites. Page 422
Source: By the author. Based on Statistical Abstract 2002. Table 357.

4

_____
_____
_____
_____
_____
_____
_____

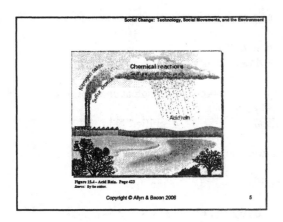

Figure 15.4 - Acid Rain. Page 423
Source: By the author.

5

_____
_____
_____
_____
_____
_____
_____
_____

PRACTICE TEST

1. The first social revolution was brought about by the:
   a. domestication of plants and animals
   b. invention of the plow
   c. invention of the steam engine
   d. discovery of America

2. The _____ is to the second social revolution as the _____ is to the Industrial Revolution.
   a. domestication of plants/steam engine
   b. domestication of animals/plow
   c. plow/steam engine
   d. steam engine/microchip

3. The sweeping changes brought about by the Industrial Revolution are referred to as:
   a. positivism   b. determinism   c. bureaucracy   d. modernization

4. The realignment of the world's powers that has resulted in a triadic division of the globe since World War II is referred to as:
   a. bureaucratization
   b. the new world order
   c. the new republic
   d. geopolitics

5. The theory that assumes that all societies follow the same path, evolving from simpler to more complex forms is:
   a. unilinear theory
   b. multilinear theory
   c. regression theory
   d. unified field theory

6. The theory that best explains how Egypt, Greece, and Rome were born, rose as great civilizations, then declined, and finally died is _____ theory.
   a. unilinear   b. multilinear   c. cyclical   d. unified field

7. According to Karl Marx, each current arrangement of power, called a thesis, contained its own contradiction or opposition which he called the:
   a. synthesis   b. antithesis   c. hypothesis   d. rapture

8. According to sociologist William Ogburn, a new way of seeing reality as a process of change is called:
   a. invention   b. diffusion   c. reformulation   d. discovery

9. Ogburn's term for the spreading of invention and discovery from one society to another is:
   a. cultural lag   b. diffusion   c. redistribution   d. synthesis

10. Transmitting medical data by fiber optic cable to remote locations is called:
    a. telemedicine   b. distance healing   c. spontaneous care   d. health maintenance

11. Large numbers of people who organize to promote or resist social change are called a/an:
    a. Riot   b. Fad   c. Social Movement   d. Urban Legend

12. A social movement that resists some social change is a
    a. proactive social movement.
    b. reactive social movement.
    c. redemptive social movement.
    d. reformative social movement.

13. Another name for a transnational social movement is a:
    a. new social movement
    b. multicultural social movement
    c. metaphysical social movement
    d. multinational social movement

14. The presentation of information in the attempt to influence people is referred to as:
    a. technology   b. propaganda   c. fad   d. brain washing

15. Propaganda is best defined as
    a. the presentation of untrue information in an attempt to influence people.
    b. the presentation of information in an attempt to influence people.
    c. unfair coercion.
    d. illegal forms of persuasion.

16. Name calling and glittering generalities are examples of:
    a. public opinions
    b. resources
    c. propaganda
    d. cyberspace

17. Resource mobilization
    a. is a crucial stage that enables social movements to move past the first stage.
    b. refers to the mobilization of resources, such as time, money and people.
    c. is necessary for a group to be seen as a social movement rather than a group of angry people.
    d. all of the above are correct.

18. The stage of a social movement where it develops into a bureaucracy and its future lies in the hands of career officers is the _____ stage.
    a. initial unrest and agitation
    b. resource mobilization
    c. institutionalization
    d. organization

19. At which stage of a movement do social leaders emerge?
    a. initial unrest and agitation
    b. institutionalization
    c. resource mobilization
    d. organization

20. The crucial stage for social movements to continue beyond the initial stage is
    a. initial agitation and unrest.
    b. institutionalization and unrest.
    c. resource mobilization.
    d. organization.

21. The 1992 Supreme Court decision that upheld the rights of states to place conditions on abortion, such as a waiting period between pregnancy conformation and abortion and parental consent for girls under 18 to obtain an abortion was:
    a. Row v. Wade
    b. Turner v. Georgia
    c. Smith v. the Women's Coalition
    d. Casey v. Planned Parenthood

22. _____ is a world system in which we use our physical environment to meet our needs without destroying humanity's future.
    a. The greenhouse effect
    b. Global warming
    c. A sustainable environment
    d. Environmental sociology

23. Environmental injustice occurs when:
    a. when minorities and the poor suffer from most of the effects of pollution
    b. when a law suit does not favor an environmental organization
    c. when there is an energy crisis
    d. when there are environmental problems in the least industrialized nations

24. Political parties whose central issue is the environment are classified as being:
    a. consumer reform parties
    b. green parties
    c. blue parties
    d. sea-air-land parties

25. The subdiscipline of sociology that focuses on the relationship between human societies and the environment is called:
    a. sociobiology
    b. ecological science
    c. marine sociobiology
    d. environmental sociology

PRACTICE TEST — ANSWER KEY

1. A (page 406)
2. C (page 406)
3. D (page 407)
4. D (page 408)
5. A (page 409)
6. C (page 409)
7. B (page 410)
8. D (page 410)
9. A (pages 410-411)

10. A (page 413)
11. C (page 415)
12. B (page 415)
13. A (page 416)
14. B (page 417)
15. B (page 417)
16. C (page 420)
17. D (page 420)
18. C (page 421)

19. A (pages 420-421)
20. C (pages 420-421)
21. D (page 421)
22. C (page 422)
23. A (page 424)
24. B (page 426)
25. D (page 426)